IRISH
PLATFORM TICKETS

Godfrey Croughton

C O N T E N T S

ISBN 0 903209 14 4

Published by The Transport Ticket Society
18 Villa Road, Luton LU2 7NT

AUTHOR'S NOTE AND ACKNOWLEDGEMENTS

All types of platform ticket described in Part Two have been seen during the compilation oof this work, but it is unfortunately not now possible to provide suitable illustrations for a very small number of the more obscure or 'difficult' tickets. In these cases however a space has been left in the text and readers who are fortunate enough to obtain copies of any of these items may care to paste them in to the appropriate space for the sake of completeness.

This paper could not have been prepared without the help of other collectors and I am particularly grateful to the following for providing me with photocopies or allowing me to view tickets in their collections:-

John Bradshaw	Stuart Johnson	Michael Stewart
Eugene Field	Henry Pryer	Charles Gordon Stuart
Hugh Fisher	John Shelbourn	Terry Velvick
Ernie Foster	John Smith	

The information contained in this paper is far from complete and the author would welcome any comments, corrections or additional information, especially any supported by documentary evidence or photocopies of tickets in readers' possession.   Any unwanted Irish platform tickets would find a welcome home in the author's collection, which would benefit greatly from the addition of a Dublin (Broadstone) platform ticket!

Godfrey Croughton
May Tree Cottage
81 Pilgrims Way
Kemsing
SEVENOAKS Kent,
March 1993   *TN15 6TD*

Part One – HISTORICAL SURVEY

Introduction

The earliest known British platform tickets were issued without charge to authorise admission to platforms for clearly defined purposes. No such free issues are known from any part of Ireland.

The introduction of charged platform tickets in Great Britain resulted from the erection of ticket barriers to control access to platforms in the interests of public safety and revenue protection, a process which began in earnest about 1912 and had spread to the principal stations in cities and larger towns, holiday resorts and many suburban stations by the outbreak of the First World War.

The population of the island of Ireland is barely two thirds of that of Greater London. Only Belfast, Cork and Dublin have had regular suburban rail services and there are few seaside resorts comparable with the major watering places in Great Britain. The need for platform tickets would therefore be much more limited than on the other side of the Irish Sea. Nevertheless no fewer than 53 Irish stations are known to have issued platform tickets at one time or another, the great majority of these being found along the eastern seaboard, with only three (Athlone, Dublin [Broadstone] and Galway) being known on the former Midland Great Western company's system.

The earliest known example dates from the summer of 1909 and the latest from early 1987. There are no longer any platform tickets in use anywhere in Ireland but this situation may change as various railway preservation schemes come to fruition.

The Pre-Grouping Era

There was a good deal of English influence in the management of the Great Northern Railway (Ireland) and it is not surprising to find this company introducing platform tickets at its principal stations before the First World War. The earliest known example was on plain mauve card issued at the west coast resort of Bundoran on 31st July 1909 with a similar Dundalk ticket following by September 1913.

The Midland Railway was sparing in its use of platform tickets in England and it does not appear to have provided them at any of its Northern Counties Committee stations in Ulster.

The first railway in Ireland linked Dublin city with the port of Kingstown (now Dun Laoghaire). Coastal residential development expanded throughout the Victorian period and by the turn of the century stretched as far south as Bray, providing ample business for an intensive Dublin & South Eastern Railway suburban service into Harcourt Street and Westland Row. The select residential resort of Greystones was issuing platform tickets by August 1916 and within a few years stocks had been provided at principal stations down the coast to Wexford and at some suburban stations. Indeed it is possible that all D&SER suburban stations had platform tickets although only a handful have so far come to light. One which might be expected to have existed is Dalkey but none has yet been seen. Most D&SER platform tickets displayed equal horizontal divisions of green, white and green although the shade varied from turquoise to a very dark green. Surplus excursion ticket card was used up during the paper shortages of the First World War giving some strikingly varied colour schemes.

Pre-grouping platform tickets have not yet been seen from any other Irish company although it is probable that the Great Southern & Western Railway issued them at Dublin (Kingsbridge) and perhaps also at Waterford. The earliest known platform ticket from Kingsbridge is No.8719 of series E, headed G.S.Rys and machine dated 15th August 1925; it is quite different in design from the D&SER style tickets in use at other GSR stations at that time. It seems hard to imagine that 48,719 platform tickets would have been issued at Kingsbridge in the first nine months of the company's existence so it is possible that it might be a successor to a ticket of similar design introduced by the Great Southern & Western Railway before the amalgamation. The recent discovery of an enamel sign, headed GS&WR, referring to platform tickets, price 2d, appears to support this theory, although it is not known at which station it was displayed.

The charge for a platform ticket in Ireland was originally 1d as in Great Britain. This was increased (by the D&SER at least) to 2d by October 1921 – probably at the same time as passenger fares went up in 1920 because of increasing wartime costs – but had reverted to 1d by January 1924. In Great Britain the price remained at 1d until 1st January 1958 but in Ireland the charge was generally increased to 2d in late 1924 or early 1925, probably on 1st January 1925.

From Grouping to Nationalisation

The only effect in Ireland of the grouping of British railways following the Railways Act 1921 was that the LM&SR assumed the Midland Railway's interest in the Northern Counties Committee lines in the north from 1st January 1923. In the south, the Great Southern & Western, the Midland Great Western and the Cork, Bandon & South Coast Railways amalgamated on 12th November 1924 under the title Great Southern Railway. The Dublin & South Eastern Railway was obliged to join the group from 1st January 1925 when the title became Great Southern Railways.

The Great Southern Railways were amalgamated with the Dublin United Transport Company to form Coras Iompair Eireann (Ireland's Transport Company) on 1st January 1945 and this company came under state ownership in 1950. In the north, the Ulster Transport Authority was formed on 1st October 1948 by merging the Belfast & County Down Railway with the Northern Ireland Road Transport Board. Ownership of the Northern Counties Committee was transferred from British Railways to the UTA on 1st April 1949. The two governments could not decide how to deal with the extensive cross-border road and rail operations of the Great Northern Railway (Ireland) so this company lingered on until a joint Great Northern Railways Board was established on 1st September 1953.

Great Southern Railways platform tickets initially followed the green/white/green D&SER design (with blank backs) at former D&SER stations whilst at Dublin (Kingsbridge) and Waterford horizontally divided red and yellow tickets were used with 12 lines of conditions on the back. This colour scheme became the standard until the Second World War although the shades varied from pink to brownish-purple and from cream to primrose. The conditions were reset, at first in 11 lines by 1928 but reduced to 9 lines by 1932. Most wording on ordinary travel tickets became bi-lingual Gaelic and English from 1927 in response to official encouragement of the use of the native tongue. A bi-lingual platform ticket was designed for use at Galway, where Gaelic was still the vernacular, but may not have been brought into use as only a 0000 specimen has been seen.

A new design of GSR platform ticket had appeared by 1941 on plain grey card with 13 lines of conditions on the reverse. A brick red version followed at Athlone whilst Bray and Youghal acquired a slightly different design with four parallel red stripes printed diagonally across a white card. The final type was also on white or greyish card but with the three red stripes limited to the upper half of the ticket and conditions in 8 lines on the lower part of the front.

The earliest Coras Iompair Eireann platform tickets resembled the final GSR type but by August 1948 the layout had been altered with the price being moved to the top right, the conditions reset and the three red stripes applied horizontally rather than diagonally. The off-white, almost buff, card gave way to grey before the end of 1948 and by the following year the red stripes had disappeared from some issues. Some tickets appeared in an earlier GSR style with three diagonal stripes across the whole of the front of the white or cream card but by 1950 a new standard design appeared whose familiar grey card with a central horizontal green band was to remain as long as CIE issued edmondson card platform tickets.

The Great Northern Railway (Ireland) had introduced a new design of platform ticket by September 1925 with a thin pink or red horizontal stripe across a white card and 11 lines of conditions on the back. This was probably printed by Thoms of Dublin and used mainly at stations in the Republic where the wording required the ticket to be given up when entering the platform. Similar tickets issued at Armagh and Londonderry in Northern Ireland bore the more conventional exhortation to surrender the ticket before leaving the platform but confusion reigned at Bundoran and Monaghan, both close to the border, where the requirement varied from one issue to the next. On one Bundoran example the front of the ticket required its surrender on leaving but the conditions on the back referred to surrender on entering the platform! The conditions eventually extended to 15 lines with additional clauses restricting validity to one hour and prohibiting entry into trains.

North of the border, GNR(I) tickets were usually printed by Bell, Logan and Carsewell Ltd. of Belfast by whom most GNR(I) stations in Northern Ireland were later supplied with a different design of ticket, very similar to that in use on the LMSR (NCC), with the station name in the centre rather than at the foot and a quaint reference to "retiring from platform". Careful control of printing blocks was not the GNR(I)'s strong point and throughout the 1930s and 1940s features came and went without any logical sequence: the stripe varied in colour from yellow to red, sometimes disappearing altogether for a while and then re-emerging very much wider than before. "For conditions see back" appeared prominently at the top of later issues, sometimes in plain type and sometimes in a cameo block. Different settings of those conditions were used apparently indiscriminately, making classification extremely difficult. Bundoran, Dublin and Dundalk continued to be provided with their own design (station name at foot and reference to surrender on entering the platform) right up to the formation of the GNRB.

It has been suggested that Lisburn should be added to the issuing stations listed in Part Three but it has been excluded because no platform ticket has yet been seen by the author.

The earliest known LMS-NCC platform ticket is dated June 1929 and is virtually identical to the then current Northern Ireland style of the GNR(I) and almost certainly by the same printer. The conditions on the reverse were initially printed in eleven lines but had been compressed into nine lines by 1936. By 1941 NCC platform tickets were being printed by the LMSR in England and examples comparable to LMSR Types 2A, 3A, 3B and 3C can all be found in Northern Ireland, the only significant difference being in the price charged for them.

The Belfast & County Down Railway had introduced a very basic design of 1d platform ticket at Newcastle by 1931. The colour was later changed and the type reset with issues continuing at least until 1950. It has been stated elsewhere that the B&CDR also issued platform tickets at the major resort town of Bangor but no example has been seen yet.

The County Donegal Railways Joint Committee printed 1d platform tickets for Donegal town station but it is not certain whether these were ever issued as no dated examples have been found, nor any numbered under 2000.

The Post-Nationalisation Era

Coras Iompair Eireann ceased to be a Company and became a Board in 1950 but the conditions on their platform tickets did not reflect this change until about three years later. Many minor typographical changes occurred over the years to the standard grey tickets with green horizontal band. The title and admission clause both fluctuated between upper and lower case, sometimes with accents and sometimes without, and the word "Board" in the third line of the conditions sometimes appeared as "B'rd". Numerals appeared only on the right until 1958, after which they were usually printed at both left and right. During the 1960s the grey card developed a mauvish hue for some while. The number of stations issuing platform tickets gradually declined but some specimens were printed (specially for collectors ?) in the early 1960s for stations which had ceased to issue. Only the three main Dublin city stations (by then named Connolly, Heuston and Pearse) continued issuing long enough to acquire tickets printed with decimal prices (2p), the latest known issue being at Heuston on 1st February 1973 although an earlier type was still on sale at Bray up to seven months later. The same station rejoiced in a special issue for a Railway Preservation Society of Ireland excursion on an unknown but probably later date: only an undated specimen has so far been seen.

After the Great Northern Railway Board was formed in September 1953, its platform tickets initially perpetuated the separate Southern and Northern designs of its predecessor, but in 1958 both Dublin (Amiens Street) and Dundalk Junction were provided with the same style as the Ulster stations. Most of the cross-border lines were closed in October 1957 prior to the break-up of the remainder of the Board's assets which were transferred to UTA (in Northern Ireland) and CIE (in the Republic) on 1st October 1958, after which date the new owners provided platform tickets in their own styles.

After its formation in 1948, the Ulster Transport Authority produced two quite distinct styles of platform tickets. Those for use at former NCC stations were printed by the London Midland Region of British Railways (as successors to the LMSR) whilst those intended for former GNRB stations continued in Great Northern style. The only known exception is at Londonderry where GNR-style tickets were produced for sale at Waterside station a couple of years after the closure of Foyle Road.

The road and rail interests of UTA were split in the spring of 1967 to form two separate companies: Ulsterbus and Northern Ireland Railways. NIR perpetuated the GNR design of ticket at Belfast (Great Victoria Street), Coleraine, Londonderry (Waterside) and Portadown but only the last named received new stock after the price was increased to 3d in 1969 or 1970. A BR 2d print with NIR title was on sale at Belfast (York Road) in 1970/1 but this had given way by February 1973 to a new 2p design without hour numerals. A modernised version of the old GNR style was provided for the opening of Belfast (Central) station in April 1976 and this remained on sale until at least March 1987, thus becoming the last Irish platform ticket.

An attempt was made in the 1960s to preserve and reopen part of the former NCC narrow-gauge line into Victoria Road station at Londonderry. A souvenir platform ticket was printed with the title Foyle Valley Railway but only the child version has so far been seen.

Machine-issued Tickets

Most Irish platform tickets were edmondson cards, dated through a conventional pillar-type press, but some of the busier stations at one time had pull-bar machines to dispense Edmondson tickets. Theoretically they were dated by the machine upon issue but in later years the dating mechanism fell into disuse. Known locations and periods of use are as follows:-

Belfast (Great Victoria Street)	before 1940
Dublin (Amiens Street)	1930s & early 1940s ?
Dublin (Harcourt Street)	1922 to 1925
Dublin (Kingsbridge)	1925 to 1931
Dublin (Westland Row)	1924 to 1932
Galway	Until 1963
Limerick	1929
Waterford	1927 to 1934

No BEAM machines are known to have been used in Ireland but AA machines were introduced by the Ulster Transport Authority at Belfast (York Road) and Londonderry (Waterside) in about 1960. The tickets were printed on white rolls; the front resembled contemporary BR tickets but the conditions on the back were unique to the UTA. Three minor changes were later made to the typesetting and the tickets remained in use until at least October 1969. Coras Iompair Eireann also installed AA machines at Dublin (Kingsbridge [later Heuston]) and Waterford using pink (later mauve) rolls of their own design, of which there were four different variants. AA machines do not have a dating mechanism but it is known from personal observation that the Waterford machine was in use in December 1962 and October 1967.

Part Two – CLASSIFICATION OF TICKET TYPES

BELFAST & COUNTY DOWN RAILWAY
(All tickets have blank backs)

Type 1A. Black print on mauve card.
Earliest date: 12. 9.1931 *Latest date:* 19. 9.1936
Issuing point: Newcastle.

Type 1B. Black print on salmon card.
Earliest date: 10.11.1949 *Latest date:* 15. 1.1950
Issuing point: Newcastle

CORAS IOMPAIR EIREANN
(All tickets except type 7 have blank backs)

Type 1. Full title in upper case without accents. Similar to GSR type 9; off-white (almost buff) with three parallel diagonal red stripes on upper half of front.
Earliest date: 23.11.1945 *Latest date:* 30.1.1962
Issuing points: Bray; Cork (Albert Quay); Dublin (Kingsbridge); Killarney; Limerick; Waterford; Wexford; Wicklow.

Type 2A. Full title in upper case; accents on first O and first E. Off-white (almost buff) with three parallel red horizontal stripes near top of front; admission clause in block capitals; price moved to upper right and abbreviated to 2d.; single rule below station name; conditions reset but still in eight lines ending "Company's Bye-Laws and Regulations".
Earliest date: 26.8.1948 *Latest date:* 26.8.1949
Issuing points: Athlone; Cork (Glanmire); Dublin (Kingsbridge); Dun Laoghaire; Killarney; Waterford

Type 2B. No accent on first O. Plain grey card; no full stop after price.
Earliest date: 1.10.1949 *Latest date:* 17. 3.1952
Issuing points: Athlone; Cork (Glanmire); Dublin (Kingsbridge)

Type 2C. Grey with three parallel horizontal red stripes near top of front; full stop after price. Most examples have accents on first O and first E.
Earliest date: 11.10.1948 *Latest date:* 2.8.1960
Issuing points: Bray; Cork (Albert Quay); Dublin (Harcourt Street); Dublin (Kingsbridge); Killarney; Limerick; Youghal.
Note: Bray, Dublin (Kingsbridge) and Youghal tickets lack accents in title and Youghal tickets lack full stop after price.

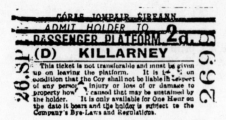   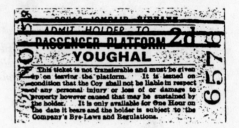

Type 2D. Similar to Type 2C but with large sans serif "A" or serifed "M" at top left and smaller "2d." to right of station name.
Earliest date: 3.8.1949 *Latest date:* 8.10.1949
Issuing point: Dublin (Westland Row) A; Galway M
Note: Galway tickets were issued through a pull-bar machine.

Type 2E. No accents in title. White (or cream) with three diagonal red stripes across whole of front.
Earliest date: 27.7.1950 *Latest date:* 12.4.1956
Issuing points: Cork (Glanmire); Dublin (Kingsbridge); Dun Laoghaire; Galway
Note: Dun Laoghaire tickets have a rule above, rather than below station name.

Type 2F. Similar to Type 2E but with large serifed "M" at top left and smaller price in brackets after station name. Issued through pull-bar machine.
Earliest date: no dated example seen.
Issuing point: Galway M

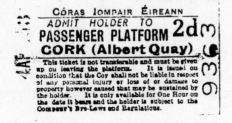

Type 2G. Larger initial letters in title with accents on first O and first E. Grey with central horizontal green band on front.
Earliest date: 24.7.1950 *Latest date:* 4.4.1953
Issuing points: Cork (Albert Quay); Dublin (Kingsbridge); Limerick; Waterford; Wexford

S N C F

PLATFORM TICKET
issuing stations

Originally compiled from list
ex-HEP possibly ex-JLK/MGS;
supplementary information from
LD, SWJ and SNCF.
         First typed 1982 [?].
NB: name renderings may differ
on actual tickets i.e. this is a list of
stations rather than tickets. Most
accents ignored (or were not
shown on list).

Abancourt
Abbeville
Achiet
Agen
L'Aigle
Aillevilliers
Ailly-sur-Noye
Aix-en-Provence
Aix-les-Bains (Le Revard)
Albert
Albertville
Albi-Ville
Alencon
Ales
Altkirch
Amberieu
Amboise
Amiens
Ancenis
Angers-St.-Laud
Angoulême
Annecy
Annemasse
Antibes
Arcachon
Les Arcs
Argentan
Argenteuil
Argenton-sur-Creuse
Arles
Armentieres
Arras
Asnieres
Aubagne
Les Aubrais-Orleans
Audun-le-Roman
Aulnay-sous-Bois
Aulnoye
Auray
Aurillac
Autun
Auxerre-Saint-Gervais
Avignon
Avranches

Baccarat
Bains-les-Bains
Bale (Suisse)
Bar-le-Duc
Baroncourt
Bar-sur-Aube
Batz-sur-Mer
La Baule - Escoublac
La Baule-les-Pins
Bayeux
Bayonne
Beaugency
Beaulieu-sur-Mer
Beaune
Beauvais
Becon-les-Bruyeres
Bedarieux
Bel-Air
Belfort
Bellegarde (Ain)
Bening
Bergerac
Berlaimont
Bernay
Besançon-Viotte
Béthune
Bezieres
Biarritz-la-Negresse
Bitche
Blainville-Damelevieres
Blois
Bohain
Boissy St. Leger
Bordeaux-St.-Jean
Boulogne (Tintelleries)
Boulogne-Ville
(Bourg-en-Bresse
(Bourg (Ain)
Bourges
Bourg-st-Maurice
Boussens
Breaute-Beauzville
Bressuire
Brest
Brioude
Briouze
Brive-la-Gaillarde
Brunoy
Bruyeres (Vosges)
Busigny

Caen
Cagnes-sur-Mer
Cahors
Calais-Ville
Cambrai
Campsie
Cannes
Carcassonne
Carentan
Carignan
Carmaux
Carnoles

Castelnaudary
Castres (Tarn)
Caudry
Cerbere
Cernay (Haut-Rhin)
Chagny
Châlons-sur-Marne
Chalon-sur-Saone
Chambery-Ch.-les-Eaux
Chamonix-Mt-Blanc
Champ-de-Courses-d'Enghien
Chantilly-Gouvieux
Charleville-Mezieres
Charmes (Vosges)
Chartres
Chateau-du-Loir
Chateaulin-Embranchment
Chateau Migny
Chateauneuf-sur-Charente
Chateauroux
Chateau-Thierry
Chatellerault
Chatel-Nomexy
Chaumont
Chauny
Chelles-Gournay
Cherbourg
Choisy-le-Roi
Cholet
Clermont-de-l'Oise
Clermont-Ferrand
Cluses (Haute-Savoie)
Cognac
Colmar
Colombes
Commercy
Compiegne
Conches
Conflans-Jarny
Contres
Contrexeville
Corbie
Cosne
Coutances
Coutras
Creil
Crepy-en-Valois
Le Creusot
La Croisac
Culmont-Chalindrey
Culoz

Dax
Decize
La Defense
Deluz
Diemeringen
Dieppe
Dijon-Ville
Dinan
Dinard
Dol
Dole-Ville

Don-Sainghin
Douai
Dreux
Dunkerque

Enghien-les-Bains
Epernay
Epinal
Etampes
Étaples
Etival-Clairefontaine
Eu
Evian-les-Bains
Evreux-Embranchement
Evron

Facture
Faulquemont
Fecamp
Firminy
Flers
Foix
Folligny
Fontainbleau-Avon
Fontenay-sous-Bois
Forbach
Fourmies

Gannat
Gap
La Garenne-Bezons
Garges
Gien
Golfe-Juan-Villauris
Gourdon
Granville
Gray
Grenoble
Gueret
Guingamp

Hagondange
Hagenau
Le Havre
Hazebrouck
Hendaye
Hirson

Ingwiller
Invaldes
Issoire
Issoudun

Jarnac (Charente)
Jeumont
Joigny
Joinville-le-Pont
Jonzac

Juan-le-Pins
Juvisy

Lamballe
Landerneau
Landivisiau
Langeac
Langres
Laon
Laroche-Migennes
Les Laumes-Alesia
Lauterbourg
Laval
Lens
Lepanges
Lerouville
Libercourt
Libourne
Lille
Limoges-Benedictins
Lisieux
Longpre-les-Corps-Saints
Longeau
Longueville (Seine-et-Marne)
Longuyon
Longwy
Lons-le-Saunier
Lorient
Lourdes
Luneville
Lure
Luxeil-les-Bains
Lyon-Brotteaux
Lyon-Part-Dieu
Lyon-Perrache

Macon
Le Mans
Mantes-la-Jolie
Marmande
Marquise-Rixente
Marseilles-St-Charles
Marvejois
Maubeuge
Melun
Menton
Mer (Loir-et-Cher)
Meru
Metz-Ville
Mezidon
Millau
Miramas
Mirecourt
Moissac
Molsheim
Monaco-Monte-Carlo
Montargis
Montauban-Ville-Bourbon
Montbeliard
Montceau-les-Mines
Montchanin
Mont-de-Marsan

Le Mont-Dore
Montelimar
Montendre
Montescourt
Montluçon-Ville
Montmedy
Montpellier
Montrejeau-Gourdan-Polignan
Morcenx
Moret-vers-les-S____
Morlais
Mouchard
Moulins-sur-Allier
Moutiers-Salins
Mulhouse-Ville

Nancy-Ville
Nangis
Nantes [-Orleans]
Narbonne
Nemours St. Pierre
Neufchateau
Nevers
Nice-Riquier
Nice-Saint-Augustin
Nice-Ville
Nimes
Niort
Nogent-le-Perreux-Bry
Nogent-sur-Marne
Noyon

Oissel
Onville
Orange
Orleans
Orthez
Ostricourt

Pamiers
Paray-le-Monial
Le Parc-de-St-Maur
Paris-Austerlitz
Paris-Bastille
Paris-Est
Paris-Gare-de-Lyon
Paris-Lyon
Paris-Montparneasse
Paris-Nord
Paris-Reuilly
Paris-St. Lazare
Pau
Perigueux
Perpignan
Pertuis
Plouaret
Poissy
Poitiers
Poix-de-Picardie
Pons
Pont-à-Mousson

Pont-Chateau
Pont-d'Ardres
Pontorson-Mt-St-Michel
Pont-Ste-Maxence
Pont-St. Michel
Pontoise
Pornichet
Port-Boulet
Le Pouliguen
Prouvy-Thiant
Provins
Le Puy
Puyoo

Quai d'Orsay
Quimper
Quimperle

Le Raincy-Villemomble-Montfermeil
Rang-du-Fliers-Verton
Raon-l'Etape
Redon
Reims
Rennes
Rethel
Riom
Roanne
Rochefort
La Rochelle-Ville
La Roche-sur-Yon
Rodez
Roissy-Aeroport
Romilly-sur-Seine
Rosny-Bois-Perrier
Rosny-sous-Bois
Rosporden
Roubaix
Rouen-Rive-Droit
Royan
Ruffec (Charente)

Sable
Les Sables-d'Olonne
Saintes
Saint-Amand-Montrond
St. Avold
St. Brieuc
St. Chamond
St. Claude
Saint-Cyr
Saint-Die
Saint-Dizier
St. Etienne-Chateaucreux
St. Etienne-la-Terrasse
Saint Gaudens
St. Gervais-les-Bains-le-Fayet
St. Jean-d'Angely
St. Jean-de-Luz-Ciboure
St. Just-en-Chausee
St. Laurent-du-Var
Saint-Lo

St. Louis-Haut-Rhin
Saint-Malo
St. Malo-St. Cervan
St. Marie-aux-Mines
St. Maur-Creteil
St. Nazaire
St. Omer (Pas-de-Calais)
St. Pierre-des-Corps
St. Pol-sur-Ternoise
St. Quentin
St. Rambert-d'Albon
St. Raphaël-Valescure
St. Roch (Somme)
St. Savoil
St. Sulpice-Lauriere
Sarrebourg
Sarreguemines
Sartrouville
Saujon
Saumur-Rive-Droit
Saverne
Sedan
Selestat
Sens
Serquigny
Sète
Sevran-Beaudottes
Sille-le-Guillaume
Soissons
Somain
La Souterraine
Strasbourg
Sucy-Bonneuil
Surgeres

Tarascon
Tarbes
Thaon
Thionville
Thonon-les-Bains
Tonneins
Toul
Toulon
Toulouse-Matabiau
Tourcoing
La-Tour-de-Carol-Enveitg
Tours
Le Treport-Mers
Trouville-Deauville
Troyes
Tulle

Ussel
Uzerche

Valence
Valenciennes
Valognes
Vannes
Vendome
Verdun

Vernon (Eure)
Versailles-Chantiers
Versailles-Rive-Droit
Versailles-Rive-Gauche
Vert-Galant
Vesoul
Vichy
Vienne
Vierzon-Ville
Villedieu-les-Poeles
Villefranche/Saone
Villefranche-Vernet-les-Bains
Villeneuve-St. Georges
Villers-Cotterets
Villiers-le-Bel-Gonesse
Villiers-Neauphile-P____
Vincennes
Vincennes-Fontenay
Vire
Vitre
Vitry-en-Artois
Vitry-le-Francois
Vittel
Voiron

Wallers
Wimille-Wimereux
Wissembourg

Yerres
Yvetot

sncfplat / 220197 / ©LD

Type 2H. Similar to type 2G but with large sans serif "C" at top left and smaller price after station name.
Earliest date: 3.5.1952 *Latest date:* 28.3.1953
Issuing point: Dublin (Westland Row) C
Note: This type was introduced after Type 3A.

Type 3A. This and all subsequent types are printed on grey card with a central horizontal green band on front. Admission clause in lower case; no rule under station name. Conditions reset with "Company's" abbreviated to "Coy's" in last clause. Large serifed "A" or "C" at top left and price shown as "(TWO PENCE)" at bottom right.
Earliest date: 8.8.1951 *Latest date:* 26.1.1952
Issuing points: Dublin (Westland Row) A and C
Note: This type preceded Type 2H.

Type 3B. Accent only on first O. Similar to type 3A but without large letter at top left and with price shown as "2d." at top right.
Earliest date: 20.9.1951 *Latest date:* 16.6.1963
Issuing points: Athlone; Bray; Cork (Glanmire); Dublin (Harcourt Street); Dublin (Kingsbridge); Limerick; Waterford; Wexford.
Note: The earliest issue only (Limerick series H) also has an accent on the first E of Eireann.

Type 4A. Conditions amended to refer to Board (shown as "B'rd" in line 3) instead of Company. Admission clause in upper case; large "A", "C" or "M" at top left with price to right of station name under which there is a rule.
Earliest date: 17.9.1953 *Latest date:* 27.8.1963
Issuing points: Dublin (Westland Row) A and C; Galway M

Notes: (a) The large A, C or M is in serifed type on Westland Row A series X and Galway M series H but in sans serif on all others.
(b) Westland Row A tickets have an accent on the O of Coras; the others have no accents.

Type 4B. No accents in title. Similar to Type 4A but admission clause in lower case, without large letter at top left and with price shown as "2d." at top right.   No rule under station name; "Board" in full in line 3 of conditions.
Earliest date: 23.10.1954 *Latest date:* after 2.1971
Issuing points: Athlone; Cork (Albert Quay); Dublin (Harcourt Street); Dublin (Kingsbridge); Dun Laoghaire; Limerick; Waterford; Wexford
0000 Specimens were also printed for Arklow; Avoca; Enniscorthy; Ferns; Gorey; Greystones; Rathdrum; Wicklow; Youghal.

Type 4C. Similar to Type 4B but title in lower case with accent only on first "o" and (generally) a rule under station name.
Earliest date: 12.1.1956 *Latest date:* 10.6.1964
Issuing points: Cork (Glanmire); Dublin (Amiens Street); Dublin (Kingsbridge); Galway; Limerick
   An 0000 specimen was also printed for Killarney.
Notes: (a) A full stop appears after the price on Galway, Limerick and series X Kingsbridge tickets.
            (b) Kingsbridge and series Q Limerick tickets have no rule under station name.
            (c) There is a trace of an accent on the initial E of Eireann on Galway tickets.

Type 4D. Mauvish grey card. Title in block capitals of equal size with no accents and no rule below.
Earliest date: 26.4.1961 *Latest date:* after 2.1971
Issuing points: Cork (Glanmire); Dublin (Amiens Street); Dublin (Kingsbridge); Killarney; Limerick; Waterford
Note: This type was introduced after Types 5A to 5C.

Type 5A. Numerals on left as well as right on all Type 5 variants. Title in lower case underlined with accent only on the first "o". Admission clause in lower case; no rule under station name. "Board" in line 3 of conditions.
Earliest date: 26.10.1957 *Latest date:* 11. 7.1959
Issuing points: Cork (Glanmire); Dublin (Kingsbridge); Limerick; Waterford

Type 5B. Title in upper case with larger initial letters; no accents on this or any subsequent Type. Admission clause in upper case; large or small "A", "C" or "M" at top left and price after station name below which is a rule. "B'rd" in line 3 of conditions.
Earliest date: 18.1.1961 *Latest date:* 16.4.1965
Issuing points: Dublin (Westland Row) A and C; Galway M

- continued

Notes: (a) Galway tickets have the station name in upper case, a large sans serif "M" and are printed on mauvish grey card;

(b) Westland Row tickets have the station name in lower case and either a small sans serif "A" or a large serifed "C" to indicate issuing point.

Type 5C. Title in block capitals of equal size without accents or underlining. Admission clause in lower case; price at top right; rule under station name. "Board" in line 3 of conditions. Most are printed on mauvish grey card.
Earliest date: 6.6.1960 *Latest date:* 18.9.1968
Issuing points: Bray; Cork (Glanmire); Dublin (Amiens Street); Dublin (Kingsbridge); Dublin (Westland Row); Dundalk; Galway

Notes: (a) Some issues from Cork, Dublin and Dundalk are on normal grey card.
(b) Type 4D was introduced after this Type.

Type 5D. Similar to Type 5C but admission clause in upper case. Most are printed on normal grey card and have the station name in upper case.
Earliest date: 13.8.1965 *Latest date:* 7.10.1967
Issuing points: Cork (Kent); Dublin (Amiens Street/Connolly); Dublin (Kingsbridge/Heuston); Dublin (Westland Row [undefined and MID.]/Pearse Mid.)
Notes: (a) Some Amiens Street and Westland Row tickets are printed on mauvish grey card.
(b) Heuston issues have the title in lower case.
(c) Pearse issues have a different setting of the title.

Type 5E. Title in upper case with larger initial letters and underlined. Admission clause in lower case; price in brackets after "PLATFORM". "B'rd" in line 3 of conditions; "Bosrd's" (misprint) in last line.
Earliest date: no dated examples seen.
Issuing point: Dublin (Pearse)

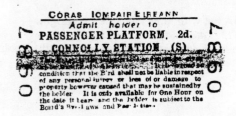

Type 5F. "PASSENGER PLATFORM" in smaller type followed by price without brackets. "B'rd" in line 3 of conditions.
Earliest date: 7.10.1967 *Latest date:* 28.4.1969
Issuing points: Bray (Daly); Dublin (Connolly)

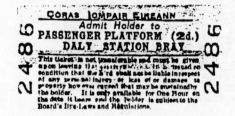

Type 5G. As Type 5F but with capital "Holder" instead of "holder" and price in brackets. Some examples have the station name in lower case.
Earliest date: 4.6.1968 *Latest date:* 15.9.1973
Issuing points: Bray (Daly); Cork (Kent); Dublin (Connolly); Dublin (Pearse); Dundalk (Clarke)
Notes: (a) Dundalk (Clarke) tickets numbered 4109 and upwards have a rule under the last line of the Conditions.
(b) Dublin (Pearse) issues have the station name in lower case.
(c) Dublin (Connolly) tickets have "SERIES T" in brackets under the station name.

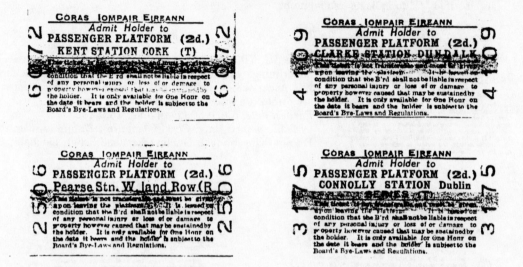

Type 5H. Similar to Type 5G but no rule under title. "Board" in line 3 of Conditions.
Earliest date: 30.1.1972 *Latest date:* 30.1.1972
Issuing points: Dublin (Pearse) - station name in lower case. Gorey - station name in upper case

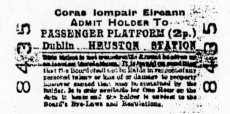

Type 6A. Title in lower case; numerals at right only. Admission clause in upper case; decimal price (2p.). "Board" in line 3 of Conditions.
Earliest date: no dated examples seen.
Issuing points: Dublin (Connolly); Dublin (Heuston)

Type 6B. As Type 6A but with numerals at left and right.
Earliest date: 1.2.1973 *Latest date:* 1.2.1973
Issuing points: Dublin (Heuston) - normal grey card; Dublin (Pearse) - mauvish grey card

Type 7. Souvenir ticket for R.P.S.I. Steam Excursion on unknown date. Price (referred to as "FARE") unspecified. Conditions on back in 8 lines.
Date of issue: unknown.
Issuing point: Bray (Daly).

 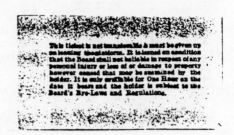

Type AA1 Paper roll tickets issued through Automation Association (AA) machines. Printed on pink paper. Title in upper case. Code "C57" at foot.
Earliest date: no dated specimens seen.
Issuing points: Dublin (Kingsbridge); Waterford

Type AA2 Conditions reset and no code at foot. Printed on mauve paper.
Earliest date: .10.1967 *Latest date:* .10.1967
Issuing points: Dublin (Kingsbridge); Waterford

Type AA3 Title in lower case. Revised layout within frame. Mauve paper.
Earliest date: no dated examples seen.
Issuing point: Dublin (Heuston)

Type AA4 Title in upper case. Text again reset within revised frame. Mauve paper.
Earliest date: no dated examples known.
Issuing point: Dublin (Heuston)

COUNTY DONEGAL RAILWAYS JOINT COMMITTEE
(All tickets have blank backs)

Type 1. Three equal horizontal bands (cream; white; cream) both front and back.
Earliest date: no dated example seen
Issuing point: Donegal

DUBLIN & SOUTH EASTERN RAILWAY
(All tickets have blank backs)

Type 1A. Three equal horizontal bands (green; white; green) both front and back. Station name in upper case.
Earliest date: 5.8.1916 *Latest date:* 5.8.1916
Issuing point: Greystones

Type 1B. Colours reversed: white; green; white. Station name in lower case.
Earliest date: 10.1917 *Latest date:* 10.1917
Issuing point: Greystones

Type 1C. As Type 1B but station name in upper case.
Earliest date: 5.5.1918 *Latest date:* 5.5.1918
Issuing point: Greystones

Type 1D. White with one diagonal pink stripe front and back. Station name in lower case.
Earliest date: 2.6.1918 *Latest date:* 4.7.1919
Issuing point: Greystones

Type 2A. Price repositioned above station name. Cream and green in equal horizontal divisions on front; cream back. Station name in lower case.
Earliest date: 28.11.1919 *Latest date:* 8.3.1920
Issuing point: Greystones

Type 2B. White with two vertical cream (or yellow) bands on left of front; one broad pink (or red) band on right of front; white back. Station name in upper case.
Earliest date: 26.9.1920 *Latest date:* 31. 7.1921
Issuing points: Gorey; Greystones

Type 2C. White with broad pink band on right of front. Station name in upper case.
Earliest date: 1.10.1920 *Latest date:* 1.10.1920
Issuing point: Greystones

Type 2D. White with two broad vertical bands (green to left of centre; yellow to right of centre) on front. Station name in upper or lower case.
Earliest date: 20.2.1921 *Latest date:* 20. 2.1921
Issuing points: Dublin (Harcourt Street) [lower case]; Ferns [upper case]

Type 3. Price two pence. Three equal horizontal bands (green or turquoise; white; green or turquoise) front and back. Station name in lower case.
Earliest date: 28.10.1921 *Latest date:* 3.3.1922
Issuing points: Dublin (Harcourt Street); Dundrum - (Down) and (Up); Wicklow

Type 4A. Revised layout; price one penny. Three equal horizontal bands (green; white; green). Station name in lower case.
Earliest date: 26.7.1924 *Latest date:* 7.9.1925
Issuing points: Blackrock; Bray; Dublin (Harcourt Street); Killiney & Ballybrack; Salthill; Wexford
Note: The Blackrock and Salthill tickets are a much darker green than the others.

Type 4B. Large skeleton "M" overprinted in black, indicating issue through a pull-bar machine.
Earliest date: 17.1.1924 *Latest date:* 27.9.1924
Issuing point: Dublin (Westland Row)

FOYLE VALLEY RAILWAY [A Preservation Society]
(All tickets have blank backs)

```
┌                    ┐



└                    ┘
```

Type 1A. Black print on yellow card.
Earliest date: no dated example seen
Issuing point: Londonderry (Victoria Road)

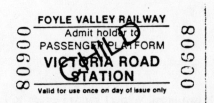

Type 1B. Black print on yellow card with diagonal red "CHILD" over-print.
Earliest date: no dated example seen
Issuing point: Londonderry (Victoria Road)

GREAT NORTHERN RAILWAY (IRELAND)

Type 1. Full Title.   Black print on mauve card; charge "One Penny". Back blank.
Earliest date: 31.7.1909 *Latest date:* 12.9.1916
Issuing points: Bundoran; Dundalk

Type 2A. Title - initials only. Black print on white card with thin pink or red horizontal stripe on front and back; charge "Two Pence"; to be given up "when entering the platform". Space at top for dating by pull-bar machine.
Earliest date: 11.9.1925 *Latest date:* 11.9.1925
Issuing point: Dublin (Amiens St.)
Note: On series Y the (Y) appears after the word platform.

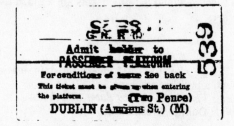

Type 2B. To be given up "on leaving the platform". No space for machine dating allowing larger print for station name. "for one hour" added to conditions which are set in either 11 or 12 lines, apparently indiscriminately as Armagh 3614 has 11 and Armagh 3660 has 12 !
Earliest date: 20.1.1933 *Latest date:* 28.9.1957
Issuing points: Armagh; Clones; Londonderry; Monaghan

Type 3A. Titled "GREAT NORTHERN RY. (I). Wavy line above station name; to be given up "on entering the platform"; slightly thicker pink or red horizontal stripe front and back; conditions in 11 lines.
Earliest date: 21.5.1934 *Latest date:* 21.5.1934
Issuing point: Monaghan

Type 3B. Wavy line above station name; to be given up "on leaving the platform".
Earliest date: 21.11.1949 *Latest date:* 5.6.1964
Issuing points: Bundoran (Specimen only seen); Drogheda; Dublin (Am. St.)

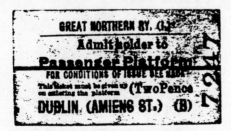

Type 3C. No wavy line above station name; to be given up "on leaving the platform". Additional wording added to conditions which now occupy 15 lines.
Earliest date: 27.7.1946 *Latest date:* 27.7.1946
Issuing points: Bundoran; Dublin (Amiens St.)

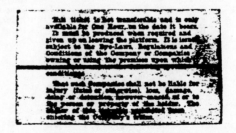

- continued

Type 3C - continued
Note: The Bundoran example illustrated below has a slate grey circle on the back in place of the usual horizontal stripe. The front of the ticket states that it has to be given up "on leaving the platform" but the back has to be given up "on entering the platform"!

 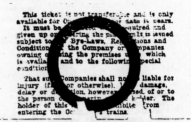

Type 3D. No wavy line above station name; to be given up "on entering the platform". Earlier issues have 11-line conditions; later issues have the expanded 15-line conditions.
Earliest date: 21.6.1946 *Latest date:* 28.6.1957
Issuing points: (a) Dublin (Amiens St.); Monaghan. (b) Bundoran; Dublin (Amiens St.); Dundalk
Notes: (1) Dublin (Amiens St.) series S and Dundalk tickets have no red stripe on the back.
           (2) The series letter appears in round or square brackets, sometimes preceding the station name e.g. (P);(R), sometimes following it e.g. (B); [S].

Type 4. Title - initials only. Station name in centre of ticket, followed by conditions notice; pink, red or orange horizontal stripe on front only, otherwise similar to LMS-NCC Type 1B. Conditions reduceed to 11 or 9 lines.
Earliest date: 20.6.1950 *Latest date:* 28.12.1964
Issuing points: (a) Enniskillen. (b) Belfast; Warrenpoint
Notes: (1) Belfast tickets are undated and were probably issued through a pull-bar machine.
           (2) Series letters, on Belfast issues, appear without brackets in bottom right corner in series N, in brackets after station name in series Q & R and as a prefix to the numerals in series T.

Type 5A. "FOR CONDITIONS SEE BACK" in cameo block at top; pink or red horizontal stripe. Conditions on back similar to Type 3C.
Earliest date: 30.10.1940 *Latest date:* 23.5.1941
Issuing point: Belfast

Type 5B. Pink or red vertical stripe (a) or no stripe (b). Back is blank despite conditions notice on front.
Earliest date: 11.12.1945 *Latest date:* 11.12.1945
Issuing points: (a) Portadown. (b) Belfast (on cream card)

Type 5C. "PASSENGER PLATFORM" in larger type; "TWOPENCE" in block capitals; red (or yellow in the case of Londonderry) vertical stripe or bar of varying width. Conditions in 13 lines.
Earliest date: 9.1.1947 *Latest date:* 16.12.1964
Issuing points: Belfast; Londonderry; Lurgan; Omagh
Notes: (a) Some issues have a hyphen before the price; others do not.
(b) Series letters, on Belfast issues, appear in brackets after the station name up to E and in brackets in the bottom right corner from H onwards - also on Omagh issues.

Type 5D. All text in sans serif type; "CHARGE" in block capitals; red vertical stripe or bar.
Earliest date: 31.1.1948 *Latest date:* 24.9.1964
Issuing points: Dungannon; Londonderry

Type 5E. Similar to type 5C but printed on bright green card and conditions on back reset but still in 13 lines.
Earliest date: 7.1.1952 *Latest date:* 13.6.1952
Issuing point: Londonderry

Type 5F. Similar to Type 5D but with horizontal stripe and conditions in 12 lines.
Earliest date: 28.10.1950 *Latest date:* 19.6.1952
Issuing points: Belfast; Portadown

Type 5G. Broader horizontal band and station name in serifed type. Conditions in 10 or 13 lines.
Earliest date: 12.8.1952 *Latest date:* 24.6.1954
Issuing point: (a) Belfast - series N (b) Belfast - series Q

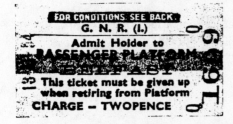

(a)   (b)

Type 5H. Similar to Type 5C but with broad red horizontal band. No conditions on back despite notice on front.
Earliest date: 19.6.1952 *Latest date:* 19.6.1952
Issuing point: Portadown

Type 6A. "FOR CONDITIONS SEE BACK" in normal type; no stripe or band. Conditions in 9 lines.
Earliest date: 26.6.1946 *Latest date:* 20.7.1946
Issuing point: Omagh

Type 6B. "PASSENGER PLATFORM" in larger type; "TWOPENCE" in block capitals. Conditions in 9 or 13 lines.
Earliest date: 16.6.1945 *Latest date:* 11.6.1946
Issuing points: (a) Belfast (b) Portadown

for backs see next page

Type 6B - continued

(a)

(b)

Type 6C. Similar to Type 6B but with stripe. Conditions in 13 lines.
Earliest date: 28.3.1946 *Latest date:* 28.3.1946
Issuing point: Portadown

Type 7A. Fuller title in lower case lettering; pink or red horizontal stripe on front only. Conditions in 15 lines.
Earliest date: 29.6.1948 *Latest date:* 29.9.1951
Issuing points: Dublin (Amiens St.); Dundalk Junction

Type 7B. Title in upper case lettering. Conditions in 14 or 15 lines.
Earliest date: 28.4.1952 *Latest date:* 17.9.1953
Issuing points: (a) Dundalk Junction (b) Dublin (Amiens St.)

(a)

(b)

GREAT NORTHERN RAILWAY BOARD

Type 1. Front as GNR(I) Type 7A but conditions amended to substitute Board or Carriers for Company.
Earliest date: 23.10.1954 *Latest date:* 1.6.1958
Issuing points: Bundoran; Dublin (Amiens St.); Dundalk Junction

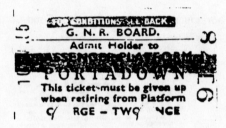

Type 2A. Front as GNR(I) Type 5G with "FOR CONDITIONS SEE BACK" in cameo block and broad red horizontal band. Conditions revised in 13 lines.
Earliest date: 10.1.1955 *Latest date:* 10.1.1955
Issuing point: Portadown

Type 2B. Front as GNR(I) Type 5E with red vertical bar but printed on sage green card.   Conditions as Type 2A.
Earliest date: 27.8.1954 *Latest date:* 27.8.1954
Issuing point: Londonderry

Type 3A. "FOR CONDITIONS SEE BACK" in normal type; horizontal rule above title; red vertical bar. There are two different settings of the surrender clause.
Earliest date: 17.8.1954 *Latest date:* 16.8.1956
Issuing point: Belfast

Type 3B. No rule over title and no full stops in title; surrender clause further reset. "Charge" in lower case.
Earliest date: 24.6.1956 *Latest date:* 27.9.1957
Issuing point: Portadown

Type 3C. As Type 3B but printed on sage green card.
Earliest date: 6.8.1956 *Latest date:* 6.8.1957
Issuing point: Londonderry

Type 3D. As Type 3B but to be given up "when entering the Platform"; pink or red vertical bar. Last line of conditions re-positioned.
Earliest date: 12.6.1958 *Latest date:* 16.12.1958
Issuing points: Dublin (Amiens St.); Dundalk Junction

Type 3E. Full stops restored to title; thicker red bar overprint. Conditions revised in 10 lines.
Earliest date: 23.12.1956 *Latest date:* 9.5.1959
Issuing point: Belfast

Type 3F. Station name in sans serif type. Additional clause added at end of conditions.
Earliest date: 14.9.1959 *Latest date:* 18.12.1959
Issuing point: Belfast

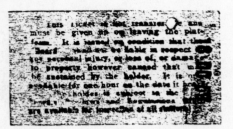

Type 3G. Printed on sage green card; thinner red vertical bar.
Earliest date: 13.1.1958 *Latest date:* 3.9.1959
Issuing point: Londonderry

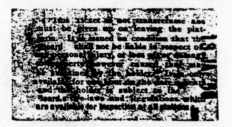

GREAT SOUTHERN RAILWAYS

Type 1. Titled G.S. Rys. - Pink (or red) and yellow in equal horizontal divisions front and back. Conditions in 12 lines. Designed for issue through pull-bar machine. Price two pence.
Earliest date: 15.8.1925 *Latest date:* 18.2.1927
Issuing points: Dublin (Kingsbridge); Waterford

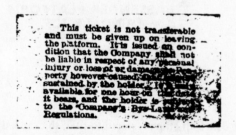

Type 2A. As D&SER Type 4A but titled Great Southern Rys.
Price one penny.
Earliest date: 27.8.1925 *Latest date:* 27.8.1925
Issuing points: Dublin (Harcourt Street); Dublin (Westland Row)

Type 2B. As D&SER Type 4B but titled Great Southern Rys.
Price one penny.
Earliest date: 11.9.1925*Latest date:* 11.9.1925
Issuing point: Dublin (Westland Row)

Type 2C. Similar to Type 2A but price increased to two pence and in lower case.
Earliest date: 1.8.1926 *Latest date:* 1.7.1962
Issuing points: Bray; Greystones

Type 3A. Titled Great Southern Rys - Pink and primrose in equal horizontal divisions front and back. Conditions notice on front and conditions in 12 lines on back. Price two pence.
Earliest date: no dated example seen
Issuing point: Avoca

Type 3B. Titled Great Southern Railways in full.
Earliest date: 28.4.1927 *Latest date:* 28.4.1927
Issuing point: Dublin (Westland Row)

Type 4A. Full title - Surrender clause omitted; conditions notice reworded; all text on face (except title and price) in upper case. Pink (or red) and cream (or yellow) in equal horizontal divisions front and back; round bracket before price. Conditions in 11 lines on back.
Earliest date: 4.8.1928 *Latest date:* 22.11.1958
Issuing points: Dublin (Kingsbridge); Gorey; Killarney; Limerick; Waterford; Wicklow

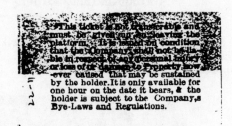

Type 4B. Conditions notice in lower case.
Earliest date: 5.9.1931 *Latest date:* 16.10.193?
Issuing point: Dublin (Kingsbridge)

Type 4C. Admission clause in lower case; conditions notice in upper case; square bracket before price. Conditions in 9 lines on back.
Earliest date: 4.9.1933   *Latest date:* 21.6.1962
Issuing points: Dublin (Kingsbridge); Enniscorthy; Ferns; Limerick

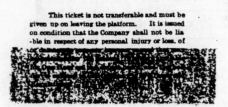

Type 5. Full title - pink and yellow in equal horizontal divisions front and back. Bilingual text front and back.
Earliest date: only a 0000 specimen known
Issuing point: Galway

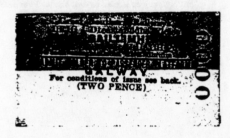
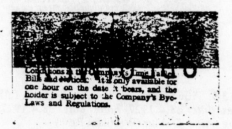

Type 6A. Generally similar to Type 4C but with wavy line above station name; brownish purple and primrose in equal horizontal divisions front and back.
Earliest date: 18.3.1933   *Latest date:* 13.6.1936
Issuing points: Athlone; Bray; Cork (Glanmire); Dublin (Broadstone); Dublin (Kingsbridge); Dublin (Westland Row); Waterford.
Notes: (a) Athlone and Dublin (Kingsbridge) series P & S have a rounded bracket before the price.
        (b) Waterford issues have the station name in lower case and were issued through a pull-bar machine.

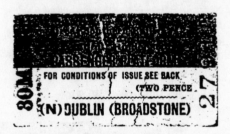
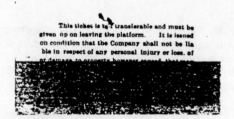

Type 6B. Large skeleton "M" overprint in black indicating issue through a pull-bar machine.
Earliest date: 5.7.1932   *Latest date:* 5.7.1932
Issuing point: Dublin (Westland Row)

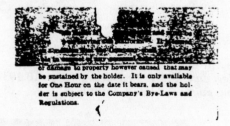

Type 7A. Titled G.S.Rlys. - Brownish purple and primrose in equal horizontal divisions front and back; conditions notice shortened and all frontal text (except part of title) in upper case. Conditions in 9 lines on back.
Earliest date: 21.11.1958 *Latest date:* 17.3.1959
Issuing point: Rathdrum

 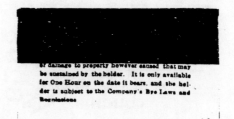

Type 7B. Conditions in 12 lines on back.
Earliest date: 22.6.1935 *Latest date:* 18.6.1962
Issuing points: Arklow; Dublin (Kingsbridge); Dublin (Westland Row); Dun Laoghaire; Limerick; Youghal
Note: Waterford tickets were issued through a pull-bar machine.

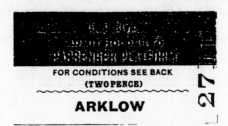 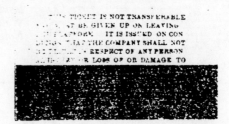

Type 7C. As Type 7B but with black skeleton "M" overprint indicating issue through a pull-bar machine.
Earliest date: no dated examples seen
Issuing point: Dublin (Westland Row)

 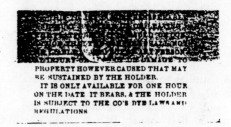

Type 7D. Front similar to Type 7B but on plain grey card with 13 lines of conditions on back.
Earliest date: 23.6.1941 *Latest date:* 18.7.1946
Issuing points: Cork (Glanmire); Dublin (Harcourt Street); Dun Laoghaire

 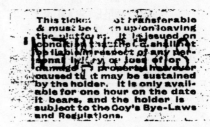

Type 7E. On brick red card with price moved above conditions notice.
Earliest date: 26.3.1943 *Latest date:* 30.3.1943
Issuing point: Athlone

Type 8. Title - initials only. White with four parallel diagonal red stripes across whole of front. "PLATFORM" on separate line from "PASSENGER" with additional wavy line below.
Earliest date: 26.3.1943 *Latest date:* 4.7.1949
Issuing points: Bray; Youghal

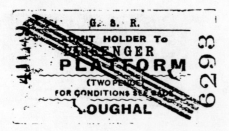

Type 9. Title - initials only. White with three diagonal red stripes on upper half of front. Revised layout with 8 lines of conditions on front. Back blank.
Earliest date: 6.4.1944 *Latest date:* 27.12.1955
Issuing points: Athlone; Dublin (Kingsbridge); Galway; Waterford
Note: Galway tickets are on an off-white, almost grey, card.

LONDON MIDLAND & SCOTTISH RAILWAY
- NORTHERN COUNTIES COMMITTEE

Type 1A. Similar to GNR(I) Type 4 but surrender clause in small type and two dashes between "Charge" and "Twopence". Conditions in 11 lines.
Earliest date: 4.6.1929 *Latest date:* 16.8.1964
Issuing points: Ballymoney; Belfast (York Road); Coleraine; Londonderry (Waterside); Portrush

Type 1B. Surrender clause in larger type; no dashes between "Charge" and "Twopence".
Earliest date: 14.3.1936 *Latest date:* 29.7.1936
Issuing point: Belfast (York Road)

Type 1C. Conditions reset into 9 lines.
Earliest date: 10.7.1936 *Latest date:* 5.12.1941
Issuing points: Belfast (York Road); Larne; Londonderry (Waterside); Portrush

Type 2A. As LM&SR Type 2A.
Earliest date: 18.1.1941 *Latest date:* 18.1.1941
Issuing points: Larne (Specimen only seen); Londonderry (Waterside)

Type 2B. Conditions revised to omit reference to availability.
Earliest date: 2.10.1942 *Latest date:* 27.10.1942
Issuing points: Ballymena; Londonderry (Waterside)

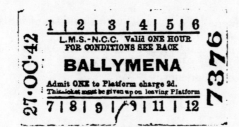

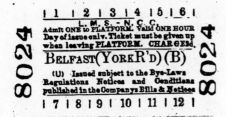

Type 3A. As LM&SR Type 3A. Back blank.
Earliest date: 21.9.1946 *Latest date:* 2.10.1969
Issuing points: Ballymena; Belfast (York Road) - (A) and (B)

Type 3B. As LM&SR Type 3B. Back blank.
Earliest date: 24.1.1948 *Latest date:* 8.12.1954
Issuing point: Belfast (York Road) - (B); Larne; Portrush

Type 3C. As LM&SR Type 3C.
Earliest date: 11.12.1948 *Latest date:* 17.6.1950
Issuing points: Belfast (York Road) - (B); Portrush

Type 3D. As Type 3B but with revised spacing of hour numerals.
Back blank.
Earliest date: 1.2.1948 *Latest date:* 31.10.1949
Issuing point: Belfast (York Road) - (B)

NORTHERN IRELAND RAILWAYS

Type 1A. As UTA Type 5C with single set of initials in heading
and red vertical bar. Back blank.
Earliest date: 23.2.1968 *Latest date:* 4.10.1975
Issuing points: Belfast (Great Victoria Street); Londonderry
(Waterside); Portadown

Type 1B. Double set of initials in heading. Back blank
Earliest date: 3.8.1970 *Latest date:* 25.9.1970
Issuing point: Coleraine

Type 1C. As Type 1A but Charge THREEPENCE. Back blank.
Earliest date: 11.1.1971 *Latest date:* 22.11.1972
Issuing point: Portadown

Type 2. Generally similar to UTA Type 3D but series details below hours 1 - 6; no overprint.
Earliest date: 16.5.1970 *Latest date:* 20.4.1971
Issuing point: Belfast (York Road) - (A)

 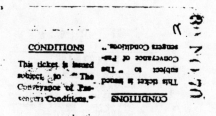

Type 3. Completely new design; decimal pricing; no overprint.
Earliest date: 19.2.1973 *Latest date:* 19.6.1983
Issuing point: Belfast (York Road)

Type 4. Another completely new design; no overprint.   Back blank.
Earliest date: 21.5.1979 *Latest date:* 13.3.1987
Issuing point: Belfast (Central)

ULSTER TRANSPORT AUTHORITY

Type 1A. As LMS-NCC Type 3D. Back blank.
Earliest date: 4.2.1950 *Latest date:* 5.7.1962
Issuing points: Belfast (York Road) - (A) & (B); Londonderry (Waterside); Portrush

Type 1B. Front similar to LMS-NCC Type 3C with the addition of "NOT VALID IN TRAINS".   "Not transferable" in lower case on back.
Earliest date: 18.6.1951   *Latest date:* 13. 7.1952
Issuing points: Belfast (York Road) - (B); Londonderry (Waterside)

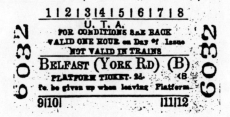 

Type 2. Front as British Railways (M) style.   Conditions similar to Type 1B but with "NOT TRANSFERABLE" in upper case.
Earliest date: 3.2.1953 *Latest date:* 28.10.1967
Issuing points: Belfast (York Road) - (B); Larne; Londonderry (Waterside); Portrush

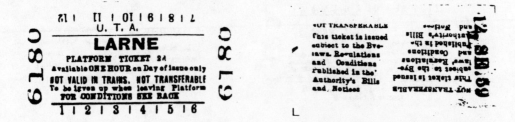

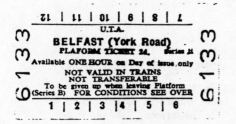

Type 3A. Front as earlier British Transport Commission (M) style: rule above heading; "NOT TRANSFERABLE" on separate line; For conditions see over in either upper or lower case. Conditions either as Type 2 or with the same wording reset.
Earliest date: 1.7.1955 *Latest date:* 20.8.1962
Issuing points: Belfast (York Road) - (B); Londonderry (Waterside); Portrush

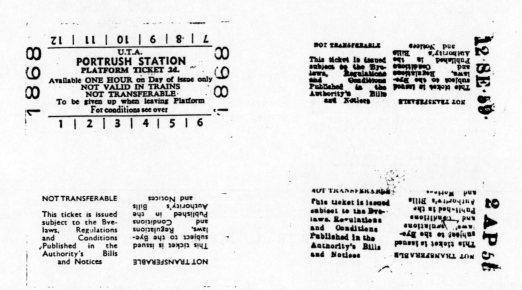

Type 3B. Series detail moved to top of ticket. Completely revised conditions on back.
Earliest date: 12.6.1964 *Latest date:* 10.8.1967
Issuing point: Portrush

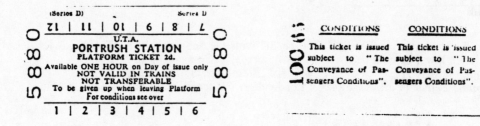

Type 3C. Availability, validity and transferability clauses all in lower case; position of series detail varies. Conditions as Type 3A.
Earliest date: 3.4.1959 *Latest date:* 7.3.1970
Issuing points: Belfast (York Road) - (A) & (B)

Type 3D. Front as Type 3C; back as Type 3B.
Earliest date: 16.8.1964 *Latest date:* 1.10.1966
Issuing point: Belfast (York Road) - (B) [but not shown]

Type 4A. Front as later BTC (M) style; "FOR CONDITIONS SEE BACK" below surrender clause. Conditions as Type 3A or 3B.
Earliest date: 13.8.1955 *Latest date:* 11.7.1964
Issuing point: Londonderry (Waterside)
Note: Series detail appears below surrender clause on series J & N (in brackets) and K (without brackets) but at top of ticket on series Q.

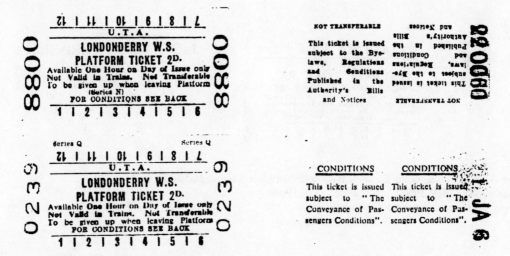

Type 4B. Front as early BRB (M) style; "For conditions see over" to right of title.
Earliest date: 3.7.1965 *Latest date:* 14.5.1970
Issuing point: Coleraine

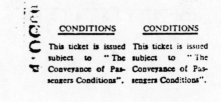

Type 5A. Front based on GNR(I) type 3 but with conditions notice added at foot; red vertical bar. Back blank.
Earliest date: 13.11.1960 *Latest date:* 18.9.1962
Issuing points: Belfast (Great Victoria Street); Portadown

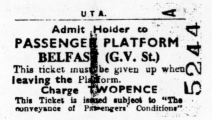

Type 5B. Single numerals and series letter (if any). Back blank.
Earliest date: 17.8.1960 *Latest date:* 7.3.1970
Issuing points: Belfast (Great Victoria Street); Londonderry (Foyle Road); Portadown

Type 5C. "ADMIT HOLDER TO" in upper case; series letter (if any) repeated; pink or red vertical bar of varying width. Back blank.
Earliest date: 4.7.1965 *Latest date:* 29.10.1967
Issuing points: Londonderry (Waterside); Portadown

Type AA1 Paper roll ticket issued through Automation Association (AA) machine. No reference to supplier.
Earliest date: 22.10.1960 *Latest date:* 31.12.1963
Issuing points: Belfast (York Road); Londonderry (Waterside)

Type AA2 Revised conditions on back with supplier's name and address.
Earliest date: 13.9.1962 *Latest date:* 11.1.1964
Issuing point: Londonderry (Waterside)

U.T.A.
LONDONDERRY
PLATFORM TICKET 2d
Available One Hour On Day Of Issue Only
Not valid in Trains. Not Transferable.
To Be Given Up When Leaving Platform
FOR CONDITIONS SEE BACK

| 1 | 2 | 3 | 4 | 5 | 6 |

Type AA3 Reference number on front. Revised address of supplier on back; later issues have rule under the address.
Earliest date: 4.10.1969 *Latest date:* 4.10.1969
Issuing points: Belfast (York Road); Londonderry (Waterside)

NOT TRANSFERABLE
THIS TICKET IS ISSUED SUBJECT TO "CONVEYANCE OF PASSENGERS CONDITIONS".   P.T. 011
Supplied by N. A. M. Ltd.,
Minerva Rd., London N.W.10. ELG. 1651.

NOT TRANSFERABLE
THIS TICKET IS ISSUED SUBJECT TO "CONVEYANCE OF PASSENGERS CONDITIONS".   P.T. 011
Supplied by N. A. M. Ltd.,
Minerva Rd., London N.W.10. ELG. 1651.

Part Three - LIST OF ISSUING STATIONS

Stations are listed in alphabetical order. Opening and closing dates are given where relevant to the
    issue of platform tickets.
The **first** column gives the name of the station as it appears on the ticket.
The **second** column identifies the issuing company and the type of platform ticket.
The **third** column gives the series letter (if any) − indicating whether this precedes or follows the
    station name or ticket number − together with the lowest known ticket number of that type.
The **fourth** column shows the earliest known date of issue of that type; SPEC indicates that only
    undated tickets marked SPECIMEN are known.
The **fifth** column shows the highest known ticket number of that type.
The **sixth** column shows the latest known date of issue of that type.
The final column refers to the footnotes below.

ARKLOW

ARKLOW	GSR	7B	2694	1. 7.53	2748	18.6.62
ARKLOW	CIE	4B	0000	SPEC		

ARMAGH (Closed 1.10.1957)

ARMAGH	GNRI	2B	3613	?		
			3629	17. 9.56	3662	28. 9.57

ATHLONE (Closed 14.1.1985)

ATHLONE	GSR	6A	0149	13. 6.36			
ATHLONE	GSR	7E	1219	26. 3.43	1226	30. 3.43	
ATHLONE	GSR	9	6575	10.12.4?			
ATHLONE	CIE	2A	4538	?			
ATHLONE	CIE	2B	6395	29. 7.50	9202	17. 3.5?	
ATHLONE	CIE	3B	1709	7. 9.53	4803	25. 7.56	(a)
ATHLONE	CIE	4B	5361	30. 7.57	8315	13. 4.68	(b)
			9352	?			

Notes: (a) 4916 exists but is marked SPECIMEN
           (b) 8343 is undated but issued after decimalisation which took place on 15.2.1971. An 0000
                SPECIMEN also exists.

AVOCA

Avoca	GSR	3A	1654	?	1660	.12.58
AVOCA	CIE	4B	0000	SPEC		

BALLYMENA

BALLYMENA	NCC	2B	7376	27.10.42		
BALLYMENA	NCC	3A	2257	?	2686	2.10.69
			2403	7. 3.58	2748	?

BALLYMONEY

BALLYMONEY	NCC	1A	8758	22. 4.49	8954	11. 7.64
			8985	?		

BELFAST (CENTRAL) (Opened 12.4.1976)

BELFAST (Central)	NIR 4	1437	21. 5.79	1585	13. 3.87	

BELFAST (GREAT VICTORIA STREET) (Closed 26.4.1976)

BELFAST	GNRI 4	N 264	?			(a)
		Q 7453	?			(a)
		R 6292	?	6293	?	(a)
		T 9567	?			(a)
BELFAST	GNRI 5A	Y 6497	30.10.40			
		Z 3024	23. 5.41	3025	23. 5.41	
BELFAST	GNRI 5B	B 1827	11.12.45			
BELFAST	GNRI 6B	C 2922	11. 6.46	2973	11. 6.46	
BELFAST	GNRI 5C	E 0219	9. 1.47			
		G 5553	1. 2.48			
		H 3324	30. 6.48	9482	24.11.48	
		I 5415	1. 5.49	5416	1. 5.49	
		J 4666	11.11.49	8312	10. 3.50	
BELFAST	GNRI 5F	K 9294	28.10.50			
		L 0125	24.11.50	2771	27. 2.51	
		M 0344	4. 9.51	9684	19. 6.52	
BELFAST	GNRI 5G	N 2456	12. 8.52	9501	2. 2.53	
		Q 1699	13. 4.54	6623	24. 6.54	
BELFAST	GNRB 3A	Q 7452	?			
		R 0958	17. 8.54	1577	25. 8.54	
		S 3379	2. 7.55	9459	19.11.55	
		T 4417	2. 6.56	9134	16. 8.56	
BELFAST	GNRB 3E	U 2510	30.10.56	5297	29. 1.57	
		V 0530	29. 6.57	9686	17. 3.58	
		W 0550	12. 4.58	9958	9. 5.59	
BELFAST	GNRB 3F	X 1568	25. 7.59	4705	18.12.59	
				4707	?	
BELFAST (G.V. St.)	UTA 5A	Y 0568	13.11.60	9652	18. 9.62	
BELFAST (G.V. St.)	UTA 5B	Z 5437	31.12.63	8858	14. 9.64	
		A 2911	16. 4.66	7258	16. 5.70	
				7718	?	
BELFAST	NIR 1A	0431	4.10.75			

Note: (a) Probably issued through pull-bar machine

BELFAST (YORK ROAD)

BELFAST (Y.R.)	NCC 1A	B 8324	4. 6.29			
		F 7835	30.11.32			
BELFAST (Y.R.)	NCC 1B	I 2573	14. 3.36	6692	29. 7.36	
BELFAST (Y.R.)	NCC 1C	J 708	1.12.36			
		X 4530	10. 7.36	8742	1. 7.39	(a)
BELFAST (Y.R.)	NCC 1B	M 2519	?	2521	?	(b)
BELFAST (YORK R'D)(A)	NCC 3A	C 6552	11.10.48	8554	26.11.49	
BELFAST (Y.RD.) A	UTA 1A	D 2107	13. 6.52	9651	5. 7.62	
BELFAST(YORKROAD)SeriesA	UTA 3C	E 0714	13. 5.67	9778	7. 3.70	
BELFAST (YORK ROAD)	NIR 2	F 0177	16. 5.70	1814	20. 4.71	
BELFAST (YORK ROAD)	NIR 3	F 3015	19. 2.73	5661	19. 6.83	
BELFAST (YORK R'D)(B)	NCC 3A	U 4151	21. 9.46	8024	9. 1.47	
BELFAST (Y.RD.)(B)	NCC 3B	W 4140	1. 2.48	4141	1. 2.48	
BELFAST (Y.RD.)(B)	NCC 3C	X 6148	11.12.48	9544	22. 4.49	
BELFAST (YORK RD)(B)	NCC 3D	Y 7579	4.10.49	8233	31.10.49	
BELFAST (Y.RD.)(B)	UTA 1A	Z 002	4. 2.50			
		A 2438	31. 3.51	7954	12. 8.51	
BELFAST (YORK RD)(B)	UTA 1B	B 5282	10. 4.52	7193	13. 7.52	

- continued

BELFAST (YORK ROAD) - *continued*

BELFAST (Y.RD.)(B)	UTA 2	C 6526	3. 2.53	8231	25. 4.53
		E 7771	26. 1.55	8636	2. 4.55
BELFAST(YorkRoad)(SeriesB)	UTA3A	F 0723	1. 7.55	9612	2. 6.56
		G 2095	1. 8.56	4909	1.10.56
		H 3880	25. 9.57	8141	24. 6.58
BELFAST(YorkRoad)(SeriesB)	UTA3C	I 1067	28. 8.58	9294	16. 9.59
		J 5527	25.10.60	9935	2.11.61
BELFAST(YorkRoad)SeriesB	UTA 3C	K 1749	29. 6.62	8221	31.12.63
BELFAST (York Road)	UTA 3D	L 0322	16. 8.64	9068	1.10.66
BELFAST YORK RD.	UTA AA1	0992	?		
		6524	12. 9.62	9305	31.12.63
BELFAST YORK ROAD	UTA AA3	A00157	?		
		A04968	4.10.69	09988	?	(c)
		D01001	?	04211	?

Notes: (a) The lengthy time span suggests that Series X may have been an emergency stock.

(b) Series M may have been issued from a pull-bar machine: they are the only undated edmondsons known from Belfast (York Road).

(c) Some tickets of Series A were transferred to Londonderry (Waterside): A05253 was issued there.

BLACKROCK

Blackrock	DSE 4A	915	?

BRAY (Renamed BRI CHUALANN (BRAY) c.1923; reverted to BRAY c.1930; renamed BRAY (DALY) 10.4.1966)

Bray	DSE 4A	4473	15. 8.24		
Bri Cualann (Bray)	DSE 4A	3557	7. 9.25		
Bri Cualann (Bray)	GSR 2C	0747	?		
		0749	1. 8.26	0756	1. 8.26
BRI [BRAY]	GSR 6A	5601	10. 8.34	5831	15. 8.34
BRAY	GSR 8	6837	26. 3.43	0427	3. 7.46
BRAY	CIE 1	7379	12. 9.49	7803	28. 7.50
BRAY	CIE 2C	8841	14. 4.52		
BRAY	CIE 3B	9427	1. 7.53	1810	16. 6.63
BRAY	CIE 5C	6631	1. 8.65	9157	30.10.67
DALY STATION BRAY	CIE 5F	0545	28. 4.69		
DALY STATION BRAY	CIE 5G	2486	?		
		2498	2. 7.72	2560	15. 9.73
BRAY	CIE 7	0000	SPEC		

BUNDORAN (Closed 1.10.1957)

Bundoran	GNRI 1	2130	31. 7.09		
		B 2884	12. 9.16		
BUNDORAN	GNRI 3B	E 0000	SPEC		
BUNDORAN	GNRI 3C	6021	27. 7.46	6026	27. 7.46
BUNDORAN	GNRI 3D	8784	28. 6.52		
BUNDORAN	GNRB 1	3610	22. 8.56	3794	17. 7.57

CLONES

CLONES	GNRI 2B	3032	?	3041	?

COLERAINE

COLERAINE	NCC 1A	A 3793	18. 6.56	4212	16. 8.64
				4246	?
COLERAINE	UTA 4B	4264	3. 7.65	4487	14. 5.70
COLERAINE	NIR 1B	4504	3. 8.70	4529	25. 9.70
				4568	?

CORK (ALBERT QUAY) (Closed 1.4.1961)

CORK (Albert Quay)	CIE 1	5014	23.11.45		
CORK (Albert Quay)	CIE 2C	8096	2. 7.49		
CORK (Albert Quay)	CIE 2G	9140	17. 9.51	9363	4. 4.53
CORK (Abert Quay)	CIE 4B	0259	6. 8.57	0508	3. 8.60 (a)
				0556	?

Note: (a) Station name misprinted.

CORK (GLANMIRE) (Renamed CORK (KENT) 10.4.1966)

CORK	GSR 6A	Y 2309	4. 7.33		
CORK (GLANMIRE)	GSR 6A	A 4352	13. 6.34		
		B 0002	24. 8.34		
CORK (GLANMIRE)	GSR 7D	Q 8401	23. 6.41		
CORK (Glanmire)	CIE 2A	8992 M	26. 8.48		
CORK (Glanmire Rd.)	CIE 2B	Q 1334	12.10.49		
CORK (Glanmire Rd.)	CIE 2E	5237 R	9. 8.50	5238	9. 8.50
CORK (Glanmire Rd.)	CIE 3B	8222 U	11. 2.52	9849	15. 4.52
		1120 V	30. 4.52	1620	18. 5.52
		9867 W	4. 4.53		
CORK	CIE 4C	0000	SPEC		
CORK (Glanmire Rd.)	CIE 4C	2984 F	30. 7.5?	9911	7.10.57
CORK (Glanmire Rd.)	CIE 5A	5059 G	28. 2.58	8355	31. 5.58
		8636 H	26.11.58		
		6497 I	11. 7.59		
CORK Glanmire Rd.	CIE 5C	1169 K	6. 6.60	6087	12. 8.60
		3819 L	1.61		
CORK (Glan. Rd.)	CIE 4D	3585 M	25. 8.61		
		2260 N	?		
CORK Glanmire Rd.	CIE 5C	7746 O	17. 8.63	9390	8. 9.63
		9876 P	23. 8.64		
CORK	CIE 5C	0897 Q	8. 9.64	5276	20. 4.65
		0340 R	?		
		0388 R	12. 9.65	5615	21. 6.66
KENT STATION CORK	CIE 5D	3343 S	?		
		5095 S	16. 8.67	6619	7.10.67
KENT STATION CORK	CIE 5G	6072 T	?	6089	?

DONEGAL (Closed 1.1.1960)

DONEGAL	CDJC 1	2103	?	2998	?

Note: None of the tickets seen appears to have been issued.

DROGHEDA (Renamed DROGHEDA (MAC BRIDE) 10.4.1966)

DROGHEDA	GNRI 3B	1875	21.11.49	1904	5. 6.64

DUBLIN (AMIENS STREET) (Renamed DUBLIN (CONNOLLY) 10.4.1966)

Station	Type	No.	Date	No.	Date	Note
DUBLIN (Amiens St.)	GNRI 2A	M 539	11. 9.25			
		Y 5950	?			
DUBLIN (Amiens St.)	GNRI 3C	B 7247	?			
DUBLIN (Am. St.)	GNRI 3B	J 9922	?			
DUBLIN (Amiens St.)	GNRI 3D	P 6295	?			
		R 9500	?			
		S 1868	?	9875	?	
DUBLIN (Amiens St.)	GNRI 7A	T 1404	?			
		V 7899	29. 6.48	7900	29. 6.48	
		W 9165	?			
		X 2915	?			
		X 6054	22. 8.50	6610	9. 9.50	
		Y 0021	?	3924	?	
		Y 6805	27. 4.52			
DUBLIN (Amiens St.)	GNRI 7B	Z 0502	16. 8.52	5252	?	
DUBLIN	GNRI 7B	X 0115	4. 7.53	5577	17. 9.53	(a)
DUBLIN (Amiens St.)	GNRB 1	B 2912	23.10.54	7119	28. 4.55	
		C 0872	19. 7.55	4392	15. 9.55	
		D 1096	?	7868	27. 4.57	
DUBLIN	GNRB 1	X 2075	?	3796	30. 7.57	(a)
DUBLIN (Amiens St.)	GNRB 1	E 1474	9. 9.57	8792	1. 6.58	
DUBLIN (Amiens Street)	GNRB 3D	F 2152	?			
		F 6251	30. 9.58	7971	13.12.58	
AMIENS ST.	CIE 4C	0541 G	22. 3.59	0543	22. 3.59	
AMIENS STREET	CIE 5C	1067 I	25. 7.60	2091	8. 8.60	
		1803 J	17. 5.61			
AMIENS STREET	CIE 4D	7053 K	9. 5.62			
AMIENS STREET	CIE 5C	1863 L	9. 8.62	3695	8. 9.62	
		1820 M	22. 5.63	8124	12. 9.63	
		2367 N	4. 1.64	6804	5. 6.64	
Amiens St.	CIE 5C	2933 O	12. 9.64	9216	26. 3.65	
Amiens St.	CIE 5D	4856 P	13. 8.65	6985	13. 9.65	
		3431 Q	16. 4.66	9715	30. 9.66	
CONNOLLY STATION	CIE 5D	3313 R	24. 2.67	9915	11. 9.67	
CONNOLLY STATION	CIE 5F	0414 S	7.10.67	9818	26. 4.69	
CONNOLLY STATION Dublin	CIE 5G	3172 T	7. 3.70	6530	11. 9.71	(b)
CONNOLLY STATION	CIE 6A	0277 U	?	0313	?	

Notes: The GNRI 2A, 3B, 3C and 3D types appear to have been issued through a pull-bar machine, the dating mechanism of which soon ceased to function.

(a) These two X series appear to have been emergency stock.

(b) "SERIES T" appears under the station name.

DUBLIN (BROADSTONE) (Closed 19.1.1937)

Station	Type	No.	Date
BROADSTONE	GSR 6A	5327 I	18. 3.33
DUBLIN (BROADSTONE)	GSR 6A	N 2791	30. 5.35

DUBLIN (HARCOURT STREET) (Closed 1.1.1959)

Station	Type	No.	Date	No.	Date	Note
Harcourt Street	DSE 2D	6612 E	20. 2.21			(a)
Harcourt Street	DSE 3	3719	3. 3.22			(a)
Harcourt Street	DSE 4A	5190	20.11.24			(a)
Harcourt Street	GSR 2A	4120	?			(a)
HARCOURT ST.	GSR 7D	P 2634	22. 1.42	9148	18. 7.46	
HARCOURT ST.	CIE 2C	R 0639	11.10.48	7575	8.10.49	
HARCOURT ST.	CIE 3B	0695 T	20.12.51	6374	30. 6.53	
HARCOURT STREET	CIE 4B	1336 U	27.10.55	6469	31.12.58	
		6589 U	?	8988	?	(b)

Notes: (a) Issued through pull-bar machine

(b) Probably released by Audit Office after closure

DUBLIN (KINGSBRIDGE) (Renamed DUBLIN (HEUSTON) 10.4.1966)

```
DUBLIN (Kingsbridge)      GSR 1      8719 E   15. 8.25                    (a)
                                     6983 J   17. 7.26                    (a)
                                     1677 K    6. 8.26                    (a)
DUBLIN (Kingsbridge)      GSR 4A     5327 T    4. 8.28                    (a)
                                     6646 ?   17. 1.31                    (a)
DUBLIN (Kingsbridge)      GSR 4B     D 5925    5. 9.31   9816  16.10.3?
KINGSBRIDGE               GSR 4C     J 6278    4. 9.33
KINGSBRIDGE               GSR 6A     M 1648    7. 7.34
                                     P 2091   27. 6.35
                                     S 3138   11. 6.36
DUBLIN (KINGSBRIDGE)      GSR 7B     V 7102   11. 6.37
DUBLIN (KINGSBRIDGE)      GSR 9      1655 P    6. 4.44
DUBLIN (KINGSBRIDGE)      CIE 1      V 2749   31.10.47
DUBLIN (KINGSBRIDGE)      CIE 2A     Y 8928    9.10.48
DUBLIN (KINGSBRIDGE)      CIE 2B     C 7222    1.10.4?
DUBLIN (KINGSBRIDGE)      CIE 2C     5006 D   17. 1.49
                                     1722 E   16. 5.50
DUBLIN (KINGSBRIDGE)      CIE 2E     9074 E   27. ?.50   9798  31. 7.50
DUBLIN (KINGSBRIDGE)      CIE 2G     G 5518   24. 2.51
                                     H 7985    2. 8.51
                                     I 9836   20.12.51   9857  20.12.51
KINGSBRIDGE               CIE 3B     J 2754   11. 2.52
                                     L 9667   29. 1.53
                                     N 8114   23. 9.53
                                     O 0113   13.10.53   0146  14.10.53
KINGSBRIDGE               CIE 4B     R 1785   23.10.54   2148  30.10.54
                                     T 5490    9. 8.55   5491   9. 8.55
                                     U 4958   25.10.55
KINGSBRIDGE               CIE 4C     V 0036   12. 1.56
                                     X 4748    5.10.56
                                     Y 9527   27. 4.57
                                     Z 0948   12. 5.57
KINGSBRIDGE               CIE 5A     6914 B   14. 2.58
                                     1637 G       8.58   9237   1.12.58
KINGSBRIDGE               CIE 4D     0087 K   26. 4.61   1601  22. 5.61
                                     0953 L   18. 8.61
                                     7295 M   30. 6.62   7319  30. 6.62
KINGSBRIDGE               CIE 5C     5005 N    6. 9.62
KINGSBRIDGE               CIE 5D     0720      ?         1371   ?
HEUSTON STATION Dublin    CIE 5D     2944      ?
Dublin HEUSTON STATION    CIE 6A     3000      ?
Dublin HEUSTON STATION    CIE 6B     7577    1. 2.73     8435   ?

DUBLIN (KINGSBRIDGE)      CIE AA1    6724      ?        23732   ?
DUBLIN (KINGSBRIDGE)      CIE AA2   47800      ?        69929   ?
DUBLIN (HEUSTON)          CIE AA3   87555      ?        90213   ?
DUBLIN (HEUSTON)          CIE AA4   28058      ?        29352   ?
```

Note: (a) Issued through pull-bar machine

DUBLIN (WESTLAND ROW) (Renamed DUBLIN (PEARSE) 10.4.1966)

```
Westland Row      DSE 4B     7591   17. 1.24   8871  27. 9.24   (a)
Westland Row      GSR 2A     4189   27. 8.25
Westland Row      GSR 2B     0176   11. 9.25                    (a)
Westland Row      GSR 3B     6050   28. 4.27
WESTLAND ROW      GSR 6A     0887    9. 7.34
WESTLAND ROW      GSR 6B     8438    5. 7.32   8978   ?         (a)
                            1266 A    ?        1326   ?         (a)
WESTLAND ROW      GSR 7B    3590 G   24.10.38
```

- continued

DUBLIN (WESTLAND ROW) - *continued*

WESTLAND ROW	GSR 7C	7168 J	?			(a)
		0339 L	SPEC			
		3950 N	?	3951	?	(a)
WESTLAND ROW A	CIE 2C	U 3657	3. 8.49	5237	8.10.49	(b)
WESTLAND ROW A	CIE 3A	V 2693	26. 1.52	2697	26. 1.52	(c)
WESTLAND ROW A	CIE 4A	W 0684	17. 9.53	8341	7.10.55	(b)
		X 2972	6. 5.57	7327	1. 9.58	(c)
WESTLAND ROW A	CIE 5B	Y 2216	7. 8.61	9889	16. 4.65	(b)
Westland Row	CIE 5D	0882 E	17. 8.65	1818	?	
WESTLAND ROW	CIE 5D	2044 E	13. 9.65	3006	12. 6.66	
WESTLAND ROW C	CIE 3A	G 4447	8. 8.51	9172	26. 1.52	(c)
WESTLAND ROW C	CIE 2H	H 0871	3. 5.52	9347	28. 3.53	(b)
WESTLAND ROW C	CIE 4A	I 8182	6. 6.55	9066	26. 8.56	(b)
		J 6860	11. 1.58			(b)
WESTLAND ROW C	CIE 5B	J 7510	18. 1.61	7523	27. 1.61	(c)
Westland Row (M.)	CIE 5C	9505 L	5. 1.65			
Westland Row	CIE 5D	2240 M	?	6207	?	
WESTLAND ROW MID.	CIE 5D	2361 N	13. 9.65	9700	16. 4.66	
		3937 O	2. 8.66			
PEARSE STATION Mid.	CIE 5D	7877 P	?	9825	?	
PEARSE STATION Dublin	CIE 5E	1106 Q	?	2152	?	
Pearse Stn. W.land Row	CIE 5G	2493 R	?	2792	?	
Pearse Station W.land Row	CIE 5G	2715 S	7. 3.70	2716	7. 3.70	
		3638 S	?	5052	?	
Pearse Station W.land Row	CIE 5H	8648 S	?	9588	30. 1.72	
DUBLIN PEARSE STN.	CIE 6B	0454 T	?	3660	?	

Notes: (a) Issued through pull-bar machine
(b) Issuing point (A or C) in sans-serif type
(c) Issuing point (A or C) in serif type

DUNDALK JUNCTION (Renamed DUNDALK (CLARKE) 10.4.1966)

Dundalk	GNRI 1	0183	15. 9.13			
DUNDALK	GNRI 3D	A 8389	21. 6.46			
DUNDALK JUNCTION	GNRI 7A	B 3733	15. 5.50	4999	29. 9.51	
DUNDALK JUNCT.	GNRI 7B	5005	28. 4.52	5014	1. 5.52	
DUNDALK JUNCT.	GNRB 1	7579	24. 7.56	7580	24. 7.56	
DUNDALK JCT.	GNRB 2A	8132	12. 6.58	8464	16.12.58	
DUNDALK	CIE 4	0185	9. 6.61			
DUNDALK	CIE 5C	0752	4. 1.64	1272	21. 4.68	
CLARKE STATION DUNDALK	CIE 5G	1812	4. 6.68	2414	14. 9.68	
		4109	7.10.69	4250	28. 8.71	(a)
				5445	?	(a)

Note: (a) These issues have a rule under the last line of the conditions

DUNDRUM (Closed 1.1.1959)

Dundrum (Down)	DSE 3	075	?	077	SPEC
Dundrum (Up)	DSE 3	152	?		

DUNGANNON (Closed 15.2.1965)

DUNGANNON	GNRI 5D	9380	?	9434	?
		9459	13. 7.64	9469	24. 9.64

DUN LAOGHAIRE (Renamed DUN LAOGHAIRE (MALLIN) 10.4.1966) (a)

DUN LAOGHAIRE	GSR 7B	8235	23. 2.38		
DUN LAOGHAIRE	GSR 7D	9774	15. 7.46	9775	15. 7.46
DUN LAOGHAIRE	CIE 2A	0839	22. 8.49?		
DUN LAOGHAIRE	CIE 2E	1207	6. 2.52	1436	12. 6.54
DUN LAOGHAIRE	CIE 4B	1660	28. 9.55	1990	18. 6.61

Note: (a) Known as Kingstown until 1920 but no platform ticket has been seen with this name.

ENNISCORTHY

ENNISCORTHY	GSR 4C	7787	31. 5.58	7839	19. 6.62
ENNISCORTHY	CIE 4B	0000	SPEC		

ENNISKILLEN (Closed 1.10.1957)

ENNISKILLEN	GNRI 4	093	20. 6.50	225	28. 9.57
				246	?

FERNS (Closed 7.3.1977)

FERNS	DSE 2D	2925	?		
FERNS	GSR 4C	0000	SPEC	7807	SPEC
		7819	19.11.58	7838	21. 6.62
FERNS	CIE 4B	0000	SPEC		

GALWAY (Renamed GALWAY (CEANNT) 10.4.1966)

GALWAY	GSR 5	0000	SPEC			
GALWAY	GSR 9	7822	21. 9.49	8939	27.12.55	
GALWAY	CIE 2E	0585	?			
		4238	12. 4.56	4840	?	
GALWAY	CIE 4C	6295	?	8538	?	
		8756	10. 6.64	8762	10. 6.64	
		9340	?	9685	?	
GALWAY	CIE 5C	0227	16. 6.66	0339	18. 9.68	
				0409	?	
GALWAY M	CIE 2D	F 3842	?	6470	?	(a)
GALWAY M	CIE 2F	G 3377	?	6766	?	(a)
GALWAY M	CIE 4A	H 4949	?	7938	7. 6.58	(a)
		I 7340	4. 9.62	8415	27. 8.63	(b)
GALWAY M	CIE 5B	J 0442	?	3259	?	(b)

Notes: Galway M tickets were usually issued through a pull-bar machine
(a) Issuing point (M) in serif type
(b) Issuing point (M) in sans-serif type

GOREY

GOREY	DSE 2B	9546	31. 7.21		
GOREY	GSR 4A	9985	SPEC	9993	22.11.58
GOREY	CIE 4B	0000	SPEC		
GOREY	CIE 5H	0000	?		
		9659	?	9661	?

GREYSTONES

GREYSTONES	DSE 1A	2089	5. 8.16		
Greystones	DSE 1B	4934	10.17		
GREYSTONES	DSE 1C	6880	5. 5.18		
Greystones	DSE 1D	395	2. 6.18	8981	4. 7.19
Greystones	DSE 2A	5666	28.11.19	6204	8. 3.20
GREYSTONES	DSE 2B	0741	26. 9.20		
GREYSTONES	DSE 2C	0831	1.10.20		
Greystones	GSR 2C	6340	26. 7.31	6843	1. 7.62
GREYSTONES	CIE 4B	0000	SPEC		

KILLARNEY

KILLARNEY	GSR 4A	1307 B	?	6853	17. 8.34	
KILLARNEY	CIE 1	C 5947	2. 7.46			
KILLARNEY	CIE 2A	? 0969	26. 8.49			
KILLARNEY	CIE 2C	D 2532	31. 1.53	3300	27.11.58	
KILLARNEY	CIE 4C	0000	SPEC			
KILLARNEY	CIE 4D	5020 D	31. 3.62	5087	21. 4.65	
		5112 D	?	7311	?	(a)

Note: (a) 5112 D was issued after decimalisation (15.2.1971)

KILLINEY & BALLYBRACK (Renamed KILLINEY c.1921)

Killiney & Ballybrack	DSE 4A	2972	?	2973	SPEC

LARNE (Resited and renamed LARNE TOWN 23.6.1974)

LARNE	NCC 1C	1619	5.12.41		
LARNE	NCC 2A	000	SPEC		
LARNE	NCC 3B	5794	?	5961	8.12.54
LARNE	UTA 2	6052	9. 7.58	6180	28.10.67

Note: An ALMEX A ticket was issued as a platform ticket from machine number 0102 on 1.6.1979 at a charge of 3p

LIMERICK (Renamed LIMERICK (COLBERT) 10.4.1966)

LIMERICK	GSR 4A	Q 9402	15. 5.29			(a)
LIMERICK	GSR 4C	A 2771	36			
LIMERICK	GSR 7B	I 1480	5. 7.37	1489	5. 7.37	
LIMERICK	CIE 1	5784 A	1. 7.46	6297	9. 7.46	
		D 6210	15. 6.48	6212	15. 6.48	
LIMERICK	CIE 2C	E 1303	13.10.48	9994	4. 8.49	
LIMERICK	CIE 2G	1403 G	24. 7.50	1538	28. 7.50	
LIMERICK	CIE 3B	H 9769	20. 9.51			
		I 4215	22. 1.52			
		J 0591	12. 8.52	7531	29. 1.53	
		K 1219	25. 6.53			
LIMERICK	CIE 4B	9816 O	4. 8.56	9861	4. 8.56	
LIMERICK	CIE 4C	0000	SPEC			
		2899 P	29. 8.56			
		5589 Q	7. 8.57			
LIMERICK	CIE 5A	1264 R	26.10.57	8640	3. 6.58	
		6851 S	26.11.58			
LIMERICK	CIE 4D	5670 V	7. 1.62	8863	4.10.66	
				8880	?	

Note: (a) Issued through pull-bar machine

LONDONDERRY (FOYLE ROAD) (Closed 15.2.1965)

LONDONDERRY	GNRI 2B	A 7075	3. 1.36	9427	22. 6.40
LONDONDERRY	GNRI 5D	6187	31. 1.48	6448	30. 6.48
LONDONDERRY	GNRI 5C	7226	6.11.49	8148	11. 7.50
LONDONDERRY	GNRI 5E	1862	7. 1.52	2514	13. 6.52
LONDONDERRY	GNRB 2B	3207	27. 8.54	3208	27. 8.54
LONDONDERRY	GNRB 3C	0385	1. 6.56	4645	13. 9.57
LONDONDERRY	GNRB 3G	5064	13. 1.58	8026	3. 9.59
LONDONDERRY (F.RD.)	UTA 5B	1424	17. 8.60	9280	13. 7.64
				9924	?
LONDONDERRY (F Rd)	UTA 5B	0155	?	0160	?

LONDONDERRY (VICTORIA ROAD)   [Issued by Preservation Society after closure]

VICTORIA ROAD STATION	FV 1A		
VICTORIA ROAD STATION	FV 1B	00608	?

LONDONDERRY (WATERSIDE) (Resited and renamed LONDONDERRY 24.2.1980)

L'DERRY (W.S.)	NCC 1C	D5136	19. 7.37			
LONDONDERRY (W.S.)	NCC 1A	M 7017	25. 7.39			
LONDONDERRY (W.S.)	NCC 2A	E 7356	18. 1.41			
LONDONDERRY (W.S.)	NCC 2B	F 8324	2.10.42	8633	27.10.42	
LONDONDERRY (W.S.)	UTA 1A	D 1070	10. 1.51			
LONDONDERRY (W.S.)	UTA 1B	D 4844	4. 8.51			(a)
		E 2563	18. 6.51	8127	13. 6.52	
LONDONDERRY (W.S.)	UTA 2	G 8754	31. 3.53			
		I 4827	16. 6.54			
LONDONDERRY W.S.	UTA 4A	J 2095	13. 8.55	8706	2. 4.56	
		K 0003	5. 5.56	4234	16. 8.56	
LONDONDERRY	UTA 3A	L 3431	19. 7.57	7366	27. 9.57	
		M 0420	10. 3.58	2531	9. 6.58	
LONDONDERRY W.S.	UTA 4A	N 8799	16. 8.60	8800	16. 8.60	
		O 0139	22. 1.60	5146	28. 8.61	
		P 0166	?	8413	?	
		Q 0239	11. 7.64	3981	13. 4.65	
		Q 4869	?	9989	?	
LONDONDERRY	UTA 5C	R 0740	?			
		R 4476	29.10.67	4481	29.10.67	
LONDONDERRY	NIR 1A	R 5239	23. 2.68	7944	23. 9.68	
		0449	?			
LONDONDERRY	UTA AA1	A00373	22.10.60	09022	?	
LONDONDERRY	UTA AA2	B00810	13. 9.62	04893	11. 1.64	
		B09220	?	09283	?	
LONDONDERRY	UTA AA3	C00478	?	07857	?	

Note: (a) May have been issued out of sequence or with incorrect date

LURGAN (Renamed LURGAN (CRAIGAVON EAST) 29.6.1970)

LURGAN	GNRI 5C	0657	?	0658	?
		0700	18. 9.57	0731	?
		0904	SPEC	0933	SPEC

MONAGHAN (Closed 14.10.1957)

MONAGHAN	GNRI 2B	1125	20. 1.33		
MONAGHAN	GNRI 3A	2550	21. 5.34		
MONAGHAN	GNRI 3D	5555	3. 9.56	5557	3. 9.56

NEWCASTLE (Closed 2.5.1955)

| NEWCASTLE | BCD 1A | 333 | 12. 9.31 | 7489 | 19. 9.36 |
| NEWCASTLE | BCD 1B | 4207 | 10.11.49 | 4441 | 15. 1.50 |

OMAGH (Closed 15.2.1965)

OMAGH	GNRI 6A	F 1403	26. 6.46	1485	20. 7.46
		F 1953	?		
OMAGH	GNRI 5C	F 2081	19. 6.52	2711	16.12.64

PORTADOWN (Resited and renamed PORTADOWN (CRAIGAVON WEST) 5.10.1970)

PORTADOWN	GNRI 6B	7829	16. 6.45		
PORTADOWN	GNRI 6C	9672	28. 3.46		
PORTADOWN	GNRI 5B	4395	?		
PORTADOWN	GNRI 5F	5823	26. 2.52	5829	26. 2.52
PORTADOWN	GNRI 5H	6005	19. 6.52		
PORTADOWN	GNRB 2A	9178	10. 1.55		
PORTADOWN	GNRB 3B	0524	?	0526	?
		0557	24. 6.56	1260	27. 9.57
PORTADOWN	UTA 5A	2705	10.11.61	2960	13. 9.62
PORTADOWN	UTA 5B	3251	31.12.63	3454	12. 9.64
PORTADOWN	UTA 5C	4123	4. 7.65	5819	9. 9.67
PORTADOWN	NIR 1A	6231	11.10.68	6887	13. 9.70
PORTADOWN	NIR 1C	7041	11. 1.71	7128	22.11.72

PORTRUSH (De-staffed 9.6.1969)

PORTRUSH	NCC 1A	E 3435	31. 7.34		
PORTRUSH	NCC 1C	I 3719	25. 6.39		
PORTRUSH	NCC 3B	8095	24. 1.48		
PORTRUSH	NCC 3C	A 4223	22. 4.49	9664	17. 6.50
PORTRUSH	UTA 1A	B 4151	14.11.50		
PORTRUSH	UTA 2	C 6488	30. 8.55	6669	24. 4.56
PORTRUSH STATION	UTA 3A	9309	16. 9.57	1869	12. 9.59
PORTRUSH	UTA 3A	D 2740	16. 8.60	4988	20. 8.62
PORTRUSH STATION	UTA 3B	5825 D	12. 6.64	7299	10. 8.67

RATHDRUM

RATHDRUM	GSR 7A	4627	?	4629	SPEC
		4641	21.11.58	4644	17. 3.59
RATHDRUM	CIE 4B	0000	SPEC		

SALTHILL (Closed 12.9.1960)

| Salthill | DSE 4A | 272 | ? |

WARRENPOINT (Closed 4.1.1965)

| WARRENPOINT | GNRI 4 | 5199 | 19. 8.54 | 5404 | 28.12.64 |

WATERFORD (Renamed WATERFORD (PLUNKETT) 10.4.1966)

WATERFORD	GSR 1	8663 E	18. 2.27			(a)
WATERFORD	GSR 4A	2530 ?	26. 7.29			(a)
Waterford	GSR 6A	R 3183	20. 6.34	6048	17. 8.34	(a)
WATERFORD	GSR 7B	V 4374	22. 6.35			(a)
WATERFORD	GSR 9	5830 D	?			
WATERFORD	CIE 1	7194 E	?	7213	?	
WATERFORD	CIE 2A	4028 F	?	7375	?	
WATERFORD	CIE 2G	0849 G	3.51	6628	?	
WATERFORD	CIE 3B	2683 H	?	4589	?	
WATERFORD	CIE 4B	1221 J	?			
		9468 J	1.10.58	9621	?	
WATERFORD	CIE 5A	1459 K	?	5005	12.58	
WATERFORD	CIE 4D	3373 M	?			
		5620 M	25. 6.62	9811	31. 8.63	
WATERFORD	CIE AA1	1760	27.12.62	3830	?	
WATERFORD	CIE AA2	00785	?			
		01183	10.67	06999	?	

Note: (a) Issued through pull-bar machine

WEXFORD (Renamed WEXFORD NORTH c.1947; WEXFORD (O'HANRAHAN) 10.4.1966)

Wexford	DSE 4A	4154	26. 7.24		
WEXFORD	CIE 1	7589	16. 9.49		
WEXFORD	CIE 2G	2941	21. 5.52	2942	21. 5.52
WEXFORD	CIE 3B	5626	6. 4.53	5627	6. 4.53
WEXFORD	CIE 4B	5322	10. 8.56	7979	26.11.59
		9864	?	9884	?

WICKLOW

Wicklow	DSE 3	856	28.10.21		
WICKLOW	GSR 4A	5063	4. 7.46		
WICKLOW	CIE 1	6262	7. 5.52	6312	30. ?.62
WICKLOW	CIE 4B	0000	SPEC		

YOUGHAL (Closed 4.2.1963)

YOUGHAL	GSR 7B	5919	11. 7.46	5920	11. 7.46
YOUGHAL	GSR 8	6293	4. 7.49		
YOUGHAL	CIE 2C	6560	SPEC		
		6571	1. 6.58	6591	2. 8.60
YOUGHAL	CIE 4B	0000	SPEC		